Heather initially pursued a career in computer science whilst expanding her interest in health and the mind/body connection. She has been researching and studying many health-related disciplines for over 20 years and is a qualified life coach, counsellor, hypnotherapist, NLP practitioner, pranic healer and complementary therapist. She has helped hundreds of people improve their quality of life through her courses and private practices. She maintains her involvement in the computer industry as a freelance consultant, and this is reflected in her logical and down-to-earth style of writing.

A HANDBOOK FOR
HEALTH AND HAPPINESS

Heather Brailsford

A Handbook For
Health And Happiness

Vanguard Press

A CIP catalogue record for this title is
available from the British Library

ISBN 1 84386 278 6

Vanguard Press is an imprint of
Pegasus Elliot MacKenzie Publishers Ltd.
www.pegasuspublishers.com

First Published in 2006

Vanguard Press
Sheraton House Castle Park
Cambridge England

Printed & Bound in Great Britain

Contents

Introduction

Life is a series of choices. Every choice you make will affect your life in some way and ultimately determine the events and situations you will experience. Sometimes the decisions you make may seem insignificant, other times you are choosing between completely different life situations. However, every decision will influence your health and your level of happiness in some way.

Some people believe that our life path is already decided for us by some higher power, by the position of the planets, our soul or genetics, and destiny or divine guidance will ensure we fulfil our life purpose. It is certainly true that there are many different ways of achieving the same outcome, many different routes to the same destination, but there can be no doubt that any decision made in this moment has an infinite number of outcomes for the immediate or distant future. They may all lead to the same result in the end, or they may not; we have no way of knowing for sure. We can be pretty certain that our physical body will die eventually, so in a way we will all reach the same destination. But wouldn't it be better to make the most of your life before this happens?

You may think it's a bit extreme to suggest that every decision could change the course of your life, but if you think about it, you will realise that almost everything we do requires us to make a decision of some sort. You may not think it's particularly important which pre-packed sandwich you choose from the shelf, but what if one of them is contaminated in some way, or contains a trace of some substance that you have an allergy to, or has a piece of metal from the packing machine embedded in it? There is the potential for serious poisoning, a life-threatening allergic reaction (that you may not even know you have), or breaking a tooth that could lodge in your throat and choke you. Thankfully, the chances of the above examples happening are extremely slim, but they are not impossible.

My intention is not to be alarmist or make you paranoid about every decision; it is to make you aware of the basic premise that the choices you make have the potential to change your life in some way. Many decisions have an element of risk associated with them, but usually we accept this without a second thought.

I was surprised to discover recent UK statistics relating to the risk of getting out of bed in the morning. Apparently, every year 30 people are electrocuted switching off their alarm clocks, hundreds of people suffer back injuries pulling on their socks and hundreds more are injured falling downstairs. So does this mean we should stay in bed all our lives? Of course not. The advantages of getting up to enjoy the day far outweigh the possible risks that the activity may incur. The key is to find a balance in our choices, and that's what this book is about.

So if every decision has a multitude of outcomes, and we don't know what these are, how can we choose? How on earth can we make the 'best' choice without knowing in advance what the result of our decision will be? In most situations, experience and common sense will provide a good idea of the likely consequences of a particular decision. And the results of most of our decisions will be acceptable, even if not ideal, or reversible. I will add here that not making a decision is in itself a decision. This may be the right thing to do if the intention is to gather more information and make a decision later, but if it means prolonging an unpleasant situation, you have to accept the consequences of this non-decision.

Choice is empowering, and whether we believe it to be true or not, we always have a choice of some sort in every situation. We may not be aware of all the possibilities, or even that there are alternatives, but they are there. The lifestyle you choose and what you choose to concentrate on determine the quality of your life.

In these pages my aim is to encourage you to think beyond the normal limits, ask the right questions to get the information you need and explore all the possibilities. This will increase your awareness of the choices available to you, and give you strategies for predicting the most likely outcome. In this way you will be able to make the best decision available to you at that time so you can live as happily and healthily as possible.

I believe that the mind is the key to happy, healthy living, and that the mind can overcome illness and physical disease. However, understanding all the complexities that govern our minds can take a long time, and harnessing the power of the mind can require discipline.

As there are very simple measures you can take now on a physical level to increase your chances of health, the first part of this book examines some of these and discusses how you can support your body for maximum health. I have presented brief facts and ideas, some of which challenge orthodox opinion, and I encourage you to do additional research into the subjects of relevance to you. The topics I have chosen are the ones I think will be useful to most people. Do not limit yourself to these areas and use the concepts to guide you to make the healthiest choices in all aspects of your life.

The second part of the book examines the workings of the mind. How you think and what you choose to focus your thoughts on have a dramatic influence on everything you do, including the creation of health and joy in your life, or not, as the case may be. As the body and mind are connected, your thoughts and attitude affect your physical and emotional health, and your physical health affects your emotional state.

I have included information and techniques to help you understand and use your mind more effectively, which can have far-reaching effects on all aspects of your life. You can use these to improve your health and to create the life you desire. Add the two parts together and you have the information to enable you to make the best choices to create your own unique recipe for optimum health and happiness.

I believe that prevention is better than cure, and by using the information in this book to create and keep a healthy mind and body, you will be in a much stronger position to overcome the challenges of 21st century living. You will be able to understand yourself better, build stronger and more fulfilling relationships, increase your creativity, achieve success and enjoy life to the full.

Part I

Your Body

Chapter 1

Your Marvellous Body

Your body is a marvellous and incredibly complex organism. Most of the bodily functions required for you to grow and develop physically, and to keep you alive, healthy and pain-free, are automatic. The average person is unaware of most of these processes, and gives little attention to the others.

Without you having to think about it, your heart beats rhythmically at the exact rate necessary to supply all the organs and cells with blood to meet their requirements at that time. If you increase your physical activity level, your heart rate will increase automatically to provide more oxygen to the muscles. If you injure yourself, more blood, and other fluids if required, automatically rush to the site of the injury to begin the repair work. Similarly, your lungs control your breathing to provide the right amount of oxygen required by the body. A yawn is a spontaneous reaction to lack of oxygen, which is why you may find yourself yawning in stuffy or crowded rooms where the oxygen level is low.

When you eat something, there comes a point when you have chewed it up and are ready to swallow it. Involuntary movements of the oesophagus deliver the food into the stomach where the correct amount of acid in the right concentration digests the food for you. The required nutrients are extracted and passed to the appropriate organ for processing. The kidneys filter and reuse as much of the water as possible and send the waste products off to be expelled from the body. You don't need to know the details or the mechanism because your body handles it all for you automatically, efficiently and perfectly.

All the time your body is working hard to keep you as healthy as possible. Cells are being regenerated, lymphatic fluid is being circulated to remove any toxins from your body and your temperature is being kept constant, regardless of external conditions. If more fluids are needed to keep your body working efficiently, the sensation of thirst is produced. If nutrients are needed, you feel hungry. If you touch something very hot you feel pain, and a reflex action causes you to pull away to avoid any serious damage. There are a multitude of examples of how your body is constantly working to maintain a healthy, balanced state for you, even while you sleep.

The human body is so incredible that it can adapt and compensate in adverse conditions. The air you breathe is essential for life, and ideally it would be clean and unpolluted. However, there are few of us living in this car-dominated, industrial climate who can avoid breathing in toxic fumes at some time, and for most of us, it is a daily occurrence. Yet your lungs are capable of filtering out many of the toxins that are inhaled, and cleansing the body of some of the others that are absorbed.

The body can cope with ingested poisons, such as alcohol, and can usually cleanse itself without permanent damage as long as the body is otherwise fairly healthy. Viruses and bacteria that enter the body can be neutralised or expelled with minimal impact on overall functioning.

It may be because the body is so marvellous that many people take it for granted and don't respect it. When we are young, the regenerative powers of the body are very strong, and it can tolerate and appear to repair a great deal of abuse. People who indulge in excesses of junk food, alcohol, tobacco or drugs, yet seem to recover and maintain their health, may not give a thought to what is going on in their bodies or the effect their lifestyle may have on their future health. Others may think that the body will always be able to recover from these and other excesses. Unfortunately, it is more likely that a small amount of damage is being done each time. This may not be recognised for some time as the body can compensate to a certain extent, or the effects may be so gradual that a decline in health is not noticed. Also, long-term health is rarely considered when we are young because the idea that we will be old one day often seems irrelevant or even incomprehensible.

In order to give yourself the best chance of physical health, you need to create the environment that supports your body and the way it works. Some people wait until illness frightens them into making lifestyle changes, rather than taking responsibility for their health to avoid the illness. Despite the marvellous regenerative abilities of our bodies, adopting a healthy lifestyle after decades of damaging abuse may not restore perfect health. The sooner you take responsibility, the better your chances of living healthily. Looking after your health is a lifelong commitment.

A very important point to make here is that we are all unique. Most guidelines for a healthy lifestyle are very general and you may have to modify them to suit you. The following chapters will guide you through deciding what is best for you amid the vast amount of information, some of it conflicting. By recognising what supports healthy functioning for you, and what has a negative effect, you will have the information to make positive choices about your unique lifestyle.

The first thing to realise is that your body copes very well in most situations without external intervention. It is common nowadays to think that medical science has the answer to everything, including our health. But this is not the case. Science still cannot explain many of the complexities of our bodies, and some of the recommendations that scientific studies have presented are dubious, to say the least. I will be discussing some of these in later chapters. With a little common sense you can do a great deal to create the conditions that will encourage good physical health.

Remember that medicines don't heal or restore health; the body does that for itself. Medicines may help create the conditions for healing to take place, but if they do, there is usually a price to pay in terms of damaging side-effects or the lowering of your immune functions. If you are currently under medical supervision you can use the information in this book to give your body as much support as possible, to increase the chances of your treatment being effective.

In the process of your body keeping you healthy, you may have to endure a little discomfort. If you are generally healthy, I recommend you treat any mild and short-term discomfort in a positive way and be grateful that your body is dealing with whatever it is. Use any such signals to take actions that will support the healing process. If you feel tired, rest. That may sound obvious, but many people reach for coffee or other stimulants when they are tired. The body needs adequate rest and sleep to regenerate, because growth hormones are activated during sleep.

Pain is a way of informing you that you are doing something potentially damaging to your body. If you take a pain-killing drug, you can probably continue doing whatever it was that was causing the pain, without the discomfort. This means that not only do you take away the opportunity for healing and repair, you can also carry on damaging your body, except that now it isn't so obvious because you can't feel the pain.

If you get a headache, it is your body's way of telling you something is wrong. Perhaps you are working too hard, not drinking enough water, drinking too much caffeine, spending too much time in a noisy environment or straining your eyes. If you remove the cause of the headache, your body will have the best chance to recover and return to optimum health. If you mask the problem by taking a pain-killer, you put your body under more stress. If you continue to create the conditions that caused the headache, you are not supporting your body. The damaging effects caused by the source of the headache will probably multiply and may cause a permanent imbalance. Your body will compensate as best it can until, one day, the cumulative effects could result in serious health problems.

You have a choice. You can heed the signals and change your lifestyle or behaviour to resolve the issue, or you can decide to ignore or mask these warnings. If you do the latter you must accept responsibility for the consequences. You may be in a situation where you have an important short-term project to complete by a certain time. Perhaps successful completion means a huge boost to your career, realisation of an ambition, substantial financial gain or security for your family. You may feel that pushing yourself to succeed on this occasion is worth the risk of compromising your health. If this is your decision, ensure you recognise what you are doing. Make a commitment to yourself to compensate for the situation after the project is finished. For example, if you are overworking, perhaps you could book yourself a long, relaxing holiday or partake in some fun sporting activities. If you are training for a gruelling physical event, promise yourself rest and bodywork afterwards. If you are neglecting your diet, enrol on a healthy cookery course.

The important thing is not to allow any situation that has the potential to damage your health to continue so that it becomes the norm for you. Some people become so accustomed to chronic health problems, such as backache, eyestrain or fatigue, that they just accept it as part of life. They assume they are unlucky, or that everyone has similar problems. They may take drugs in the mistaken belief that it will solve the underlying issue. It doesn't have to be that way, but it's up to you to take appropriate action.

I listened to a radio report recently about medical advances in cough medicines. It said that little progress had been made for 50 years or so, and a study had concluded that a mixture of syrup and water was just as helpful in reducing coughing as many specialist cough medicines. However, significant advances had been made so that a medicine could be produced that would suppress the cough reflex. But coughing is a normal, healthy, protective reaction to something unwanted in the throat or lungs. How wonderful – your lungs recognise something that will be damaging, so they try to cough it up. Sometimes more mucus is produced to trap a virus or dangerous particles, and this is coughed up along with the threat. What better way to get rid of the threat to health than to cough it up? But perhaps the medical profession doesn't see it that way.

One example of the medical profession's limited understanding of the body is the overuse of antibiotics. For decades, antibiotics were seen as a wonder drug and prescribed routinely, even for virus infections, despite the fact that they are only effective against bacteria. Although antibiotics may be successful in destroying the bacteria responsible for certain conditions, they also destroy many other bacteria in the process. A healthy balance of bacteria in the intestine is required to allow the immune system to function efficiently and for general good health. The best way to maintain this balance is to eat a healthy diet, as discussed in Chapter Three. 'Friendly' bacteria, essential for good health, live on fruits and vegetables, which is just one of the many reasons you should aim to include plenty of fruit and vegetables in your diet. When the bacterial balance is disrupted by taking antibiotics, it can lead to many health problems. Unfortunately, the medical solution is often to prescribe more antibiotics, thus perpetuating the cycle and potentially causing a decline in health. The widespread use of antibiotics has also resulted in the mutation of bacteria, and now there are bacterial strains that are resistant to most antibiotics. Infection with one of these strains can be life-threatening.

I have noticed a worrying trend in recent years where the assumption is that orthodox medicine can cure anything. Some people pay little attention to their lifestyle and make unhealthy choices, thus creating health problems for themselves. They often turn to medical science for a solution, which may provide short-term relief from the presenting symptoms. But if they don't address the underlying cause of the ailment, it will recur or result in other problems. Eventually, their neglect or abuse of their bodies may cause serious illness, often meaning that their lives are reliant on drastic action by doctors or surgeons. Then if the medical intervention is unsuccessful, probably because the years of abuse have damaged the body too badly for it to recover, the patient or the family sues the doctors! The person who has most control over your body, your health, your quality of life, is you. Acknowledge this and don't leave this crucial task to someone else.

Looking after your body is your responsibility. The way you choose to treat it can determine your quality of life. You may seek advice from those who claim to be specialists, but remember that if the information they give you is incorrect, it is you who will suffer the consequences, not them. It is your body, your life. Question and research all the information you are given, and use the techniques described in this book to help you find the right answers, to help you make the right choice for you. Respect your body and be grateful for the health it gives you.

Chapter 2

Water

Approximately 70 per cent of the human body consists of water. Water is a basic constituent for almost all our bodily functions. For example, blood, lymphatic fluid, saliva, digestive juices, perspiration, mucus, and the synovial fluid between the joints, all require water. The skin needs water in order to be properly hydrated. Water is required by the kidneys to help eliminate toxins.

Water is essential to life, so drinking plenty of water comes at the top of my list of things you must do to support your body. And it's a very easy thing to start doing immediately. Aim to drink three litres of water a day. The more water you drink, the easier you will make it for your body to get rid of the toxins and maintain optimum health.

There is some debate about the type of water that is best to drink. This is a situation where there is conflicting information. Tap water has chemicals added to make it cleaner, that means to remove bacteria, but some of these chemicals could be harmful in large doses. (For information about fluoride, which is added to tap water in some parts of the UK, see Chapter Eight.) There are also concerns about aluminium in water, as aluminium has been linked with Alzheimer's.

Many people prefer to drink mineral water, especially as the word 'pure' often appears on the bottle. It has the advantage of containing traces of essential minerals that may be lacking in our food, especially now that intensive farming and processing are destroying many of these. Mineral water actually contains more impurities than tap water, but it is inconclusive if these are more hazardous than the chemicals in tap water. Do not rinse the plastic mineral water bottles in hot water and then reuse them for drinking water, as the heat can release chemicals from the plastic which could contaminate the water.

My preference is to drink filtered tap water, but be aware that chlorine is filtered out, and without the chlorine bacteria may multiply, especially if the water is left standing for a long time. Keeping the water cool can slow down the growth of bacteria. So you have to take a balanced decision about the water you drink. Any clean water is better than none, and your decision may be governed by practicalities such as the cost or the difficulty of carrying around bottles of water. A combination of the above depending on circumstances is a sensible compromise.

A word of caution – don't drink the three litres all at once! It is better to drink small amounts frequently throughout the day to make up the three litres. This allows it to be absorbed by your body and used efficiently. A large amount of water all at once will tend to pass straight through and not be used as effectively as it could be, and drinking extreme amounts of water can be dangerous. Cold water is absorbed more efficiently, but don't drink it so cold that it is uncomfortable on your mouth or throat.

A few people have suggested that we should not drink during meals because it allegedly dilutes the digestive juices. I do not know if this is true, but it seems rather strange to me that the body that is so good at distributing and utilising the fluids and food most of the time, would be unable to cope with fluid during meals. Also, all foods contain water, but the digestive system copes very well with the varied amounts in different foods. Unless you are aware of any problems with your digestion, I suggest you do what feels right for you – if you feel thirsty during meals, it seems sensible to drink. If you do have problems, this may be an area to experiment with.

Most of the population is chronically dehydrated, and I believe many diseases are the result of toxic build-up in the organs, tissues and joints. Gout is an example of this. Gout is a build-up of uric acid, usually in the big toe, and anyone who suffers with this will know how painful it can be. The body does its best to cleanse itself of harmful substances, but if there is not enough pure fluid in the body, some toxins are likely to be left behind. The body treats lack of water as an emergency and uses the resources available to protect the organs vital to life first, such as the heart, liver or kidneys, at the expense of extremities which are not essential for survival.

There is a growing body of opinion that many degenerative diseases, conditions and allergies can be attributed to a chronic lack of water. Consider what happens when a complex system like the body does not have enough water to function at optimum efficiency. For example, if there is too little water to replenish the synovial fluid between the joints, or the fluid is not sufficiently pure, this could lead to friction, and eventually deformities resulting in arthritis.

Toxins are expelled in the fluids that leave your body. The primary fluid is the urine, and urine that is always dark yellow indicates that the toxins are concentrated and you need to drink more water (unless you are taking a vitamin B2 supplement which colours the urine). Clear urine is usually a good sign of adequate hydration, although it does not mean that your body is toxin-free.

Many complementary therapies, especially massage and reflexology, can help release toxins and lactic acid that are trapped in the muscles, tissues and joints. Regular therapy of this kind will help your body rid itself of damaging toxins that could lead to health problems in the future, or may already be contributing to health problems. Always drink plenty of water after receiving such therapy to allow as much cleansing to take place as possible.

Other fluids that expel toxins include perspiration, mucus and moisture in your breath. If perspiration regularly leaves yellow marks on your clothing, it is probably concentrated with toxins and you need to drink more water. Some skin conditions, especially eczema, are attributable to a lack of water. Perspiration and natural oils come out of your pores all the time, usually in tiny quantities. If these are highly concentrated with toxins, they can cause a reaction on the skin. This is why patches of eczema usually occur where there is naturally more perspiration, behind the knees and elbows, for example.

Drinking more water can sometimes make skin conditions temporarily worse, because as adequate water becomes available to use for cleansing, it allows the opportunity for more toxins to be extracted from the tissues and cells. Some of these toxins may be excreted through the skin and could cause a reaction or flare-up of an existing condition, but the end result of drinking more water will almost certainly be clearer skin. In fact when you drink three litres of water a day, or more if you do sports or manual work where you perspire a lot, you will find your skin becomes smoother and more elastic.

Perspiring is a natural way for toxins to leave the body. Most people are aware of perspiration under the arms where it is usually concentrated due to the location of the main lymphatic ducts. However, there is a large industry providing anti-perspirant products that interfere with this natural detoxification and cleansing process. The justification widely used for using anti-perspirant is that odour from underarm perspiration is unpleasant and must be stopped.

My view is that if underarm perspiration has a strong smell, this indicates there is a high concentration of toxins in the fluid that needs to be addressed. The bacteria that naturally occur on the skin react with the toxins to produce an offensive smell. This is a sign from your body that something needs to be done. It should be welcomed as an indication that your body is struggling with an overload of toxins that could be harmful to your health. If you use anti-perspirant, you block this natural warning signal.

So if the toxins are transported to the lymph nodes at the underarms, but can't leave the body because the pores are blocked by anti-perspirant, what happens to them? I don't know for sure, but it seems entirely feasible to me that it could start a chain of blockages that could disrupt the normal function of the glands in that area, particularly the breasts. When a colleague emailed me to say that she had been diagnosed with breast cancer and that her doctor said that the most likely cause was the build-up of toxins due to pores being constantly blocked by anti-perspirant, I immediately stopped using it.

It took quite a few days for all the last remnants of years of anti-perspirant use to be washed away or work their way out of my skin. Then I was shocked and embarrassed at the strong odour that emanated from under my arms. Luckily, I was in a position to be able to wash whenever necessary throughout the day. I was determined not to compromise my health by going back to disrupting this natural elimination process. I was also concerned because I considered my lifestyle to be healthy and fairly toxin-free, yet the implication was that my body was toxic.

After a few weeks, with no change to my diet or lifestyle, the odour diminished until after a month or so, I could go all day without any unpleasant smell, even after playing sport. My personal theory is that the toxins had built up over the years, and when given the opportunity, flooded out of my body, causing the unpleasant odour. If this is true, it is an example of how the marvellous body protects us and always endeavours to keep us as healthy as possible. I feel much better that these toxins are now out rather than trapped in my body. Is it really worth risking serious disease by blocking the pores? Wouldn't it be better to increase your water intake, improve your diet, or make healthy lifestyle changes? The choice is yours – weigh up the risks and consequences and make a decision.

Most anti-perspirants contain aluminium, which has been linked to Alzheimer's, and zirconium. Spraying or rubbing them directly onto the skin where they can be absorbed into the body, can result in you receiving potentially harmful levels of these chemicals. It is thought that they can enter the cells and cause mutations in DNA that could lead to cancerous growths.

There are alternatives to pore-clogging anti-perspirants. Many natural deodorants are available such as herbal sprays or rock crystal deodorant that may make you feel more comfortable. Tea tree essential oil has anti-bacterial qualities, so a drop of this in water dabbed onto your underarms may help reduce the odour.

Of course, if you don't use anti-perspirant and have no odour, this does not necessarily mean your body is toxin-free. It may also mean you are not drinking enough water to allow your body to eliminate the toxins. Water is essential for life. See the further reading section for more information on the importance of water. Drinking water is ideal, but pure fruit juice and herbal teas can be substituted to make up the three litres if that makes it more enjoyable or tolerable. Again it's a balance.

Don't fool yourself by counting sugary drinks, alcohol and caffeine in your three litres. In fact, the more of these you have, the more water you will need to clear the toxins that they contain. I know some people who drink coffee just because it is what the vending machine serves. They complain that it tastes awful, yet they still drink it. Caffeine is toxic and is a stimulant, which puts your body under stress. If you think you need coffee to keep you awake or alert, this is a very strong signal that something is wrong with your lifestyle and needs to be addressed before serious health problems occur.

A recent health campaign said that if you need to get up in the night to go to the toilet, it could be an indication of bladder, prostate or other urinary problems. This certainly could be the case, but use your common sense. If you drank a litre of water in the last hour before retiring to bed, it is not surprising if you have to get up in the night. And if you do have urinary problems, lots of water will encourage the bacteria or toxins to pass through more quickly. Cranberry juice has anti-bacterial properties that are particularly beneficial in the treatment of urinary problems. Avoid taking antibiotics as these destroy 'friendly' bacteria and can lead to an imbalance that may cause more urinary problems in the future, as well as digestion and immune system problems. If you have taken antibiotics recently, taking probiotics or live yogurt may help to repopulate your stomach with friendly bacteria.

When you are ill it is even more important to allow your body to cleanse itself of whatever caused the disease. The common cold is an excellent example of how fluids are used to help eliminate the virus. Extra mucus is produced and an increased temperature causes sweating. The more water you drink, the more you support the natural healing process and increase your chances of a speedy recovery.

Detoxification (detox) programs are becoming more popular. The theory is that you give your bodily systems a chance to recover from toxic build-up by fasting or limiting your food intake to raw fruits and vegetables. In any sort of detox it is essential that you drink plenty of water or pure fluids. I am not in favour of fasting (eating no food at all) as I think it is too drastic. Your body needs some fuel and nutrients, even if you relax and do nothing all day. I believe the minimum intake should be fruit juices or juiced vegetables. These have the advantage of being already broken down so that your digestive system has less work to do in processing them.

Get into the habit of drinking water frequently. Prevention is better than cure and drinking plenty of water helps prevent health problems. Allow your elimination system to work at optimum efficiency by providing it with sufficient pure fluids. This is an important step towards better health.

Chapter 3

Nutrition

I don't agree with the old adage 'You are what you eat'. I believe that 'you are what you think' and this is explained in part two of this book. However, what you eat and drink is very important for the health of your physical body. There are a few people who claim to be able to sustain their body on spiritual energy alone, but for the majority of us, we require nutrition in the form of food. The quality of the food we eat largely determines our ability to maintain good physical health. Our resistance to infection and ability to heal injuries depend on a healthy, well-nourished body.

The recommended healthy diet has been widely publicised; a minimum of five portions of fruit and vegetables per day, plenty of cereals and whole grains and minimal amounts of animal fats, sugar, processed foods and caffeine. Fruits, vegetables and natural foods contain vital nutrients presented in the best possible form to be absorbed and used by your body.

Much of the goodness in most fruit and vegetables is in and just below the skin, so it is recommended that we should not peel or skin them. We are told that cooking destroys many nutrients, so we are advised to eat the fruit and vegetables raw where possible. That sounds like good advice, but then along comes a scare about pesticides used in farming. These apparently accumulate in the skin. So what do we do; peel or skin the fruit and vegetables to avoid the toxins, thus removing most of the nutrients, or retain the nutrients and risk ingesting the toxins? Organic food seems to be the solution, although this may not be available, or may not last so long, or might even contain something that the pesticides would have killed.

If organic food is not an option for you, then you have to make a decision. If you look at it in perspective, you are choosing between essential, life-giving nutrients with the possibility of a few toxins, and less nourishing food without, or with fewer, toxins. Careful washing can remove much of the pesticide residue, and probably the toxins that remain account for a very small portion of the total toxins absorbed by your body. If you drink plenty of water and take regular exercise, your body can probably cope with these. However, the choice is yours. We are all unique, and if you think you react badly to pesticide residues, then peeling may be the answer for you.

To find out if pesticides or indeed any substances may be having a negative effect on you, you can use a technique from kinesiology; muscle testing. You will need someone to help you with this. Stand with your dominant arm straight and outstretched to the side. Hold it in this position with your arm parallel to the ground. Ask your assistant to gently push against your arm in a downward direction while you try to maintain it in the same position. Ask your assistant to notice the amount of resistance and how much force is required to move your arm.

Now you can hold a fruit or portion of some other food or substance in your hand and repeat the test. If your assistant reports that the resistance is significantly lessened, this might indicate that something in the food is detrimental to your body. You can repeat with, say, unpeeled fruit, peeled fruit, and organic fruit to narrow down the source of the negative effect. The assumption is that harmful substances within your body's energy field weakens it. Whether you believe the theory or not, I have found this method remarkably accurate for detecting allergies and food intolerances.

More and more people seem to be suffering from food allergies these days. Some are easily identified, causing an immediate reaction; others are more subtle, building up their effects over time and causing degenerative diseases that may not have an obvious link to a particular food or group of foods. Many complementary therapists believe that arthritis, ME, multiple sclerosis and other diseases are caused by food allergies. Why should this be?

One suggestion is that our bodies evolved to thrive on a diet quite different from the one most people follow now, and it has not fully adapted to relatively recent methods of processing foods (relative to the existence of humans). For example, wheat products were not available until agricultural technology was developed. In this case, the theory is that human evolution is lagging behind our technological advancement. Or to turn it around, technology does not always take into account, or even understand, some of our fundamental physical needs.

The recommended 'healthy diet' may not be suitable for everyone. Some people can tolerate foods that others cannot. If you notice that some types of food have a negative effect on you, do what you can to isolate which component of it is causing the problem. If you eat a lot of prepared foods, this may involve scrutinising ingredient lists to narrow down the offender. Allergies to dairy products or gluten can present a particular challenge because so many processed foods include small amounts of these that may not be obvious at first glance. Notice what may seem like minor effects that certain foods have. A mild headache, lethargy or lack of concentration can all be early warning signs that your body is not coping well with a particular food.

A friend of mine discovered he had a gluten allergy. The allergy had very gradually damaged the lining of his stomach. By the time his condition was diagnosed, the damage had been done, and even a tiny amount of gluten, in a sauce for example, would give him stomach pains. He said his uncle had suffered with stomach ulcers and eventually died of a stomach-related ailment. He thought it was possible that his uncle had had the same gluten allergy, but that it was not recognised at the time. It seems quite likely to me that my friend could have inherited a genetic disposition to the condition. So it may be worth discovering if any members of your family suffer with food-related conditions, and investigating if any adverse reactions could be relevant to you.

Interestingly, my friend said that he had never been particularly keen on pastries and pasta; foods with a high gluten content. He said they were acceptable, and he had eaten them because they had been prepared for him, but given a choice of anything, those would probably not have been the meals he would have selected. It sounds to me that perhaps his tastes and preferences were trying to tell him that these foods were not the best ones for him, but he did not understand the significance of the message.

I think that few of us can really claim to be totally in tune with our bodies and only eat and drink the most nutritious and healthy foods for us. How many people stop eating a delicious meal when they are full? The full feeling is a message that we have eaten enough, but there are few individuals who always act on that message. Judging by the rising obesity rates and diet-related illnesses, it would seem many people ignore all signs from their body about the foods they eat. Start to be aware of how you feel about certain foods, while eating them and afterwards. Do your best to listen to what your body is telling you.

If you don't understand the concept of listening to your body's needs, or you are listening but can't decipher the messages, there may be other ways to provide you with clues. There are some non-orthodox systems that suggest we can be categorised by type and that each type thrives on a different lifestyle, including diet. One theory is that blood type dictates the optimum diet for you. Ayurvedic medicine and Traditional Chinese Medicine present theories as to which foods are best for a particular type of person, as defined by their particular systems. These may certainly be worth investigating, but use them as a guide rather than following them as a strict regime with no deviation. They may help you to recognise and create the optimum diet and lifestyle for you.

Ideally we would eat and drink small amounts throughout the day to provide a constant source of nutrients, sometimes called grazing. Eating just two or three large meals a day creates a lot of intense work for your digestive system. Sometimes the digestion of a large meal causes such an overload that a lot of energy is diverted from other sources to digest the food. You may recognise that you feel tired or cannot concentrate as well after a large meal. Sometimes lifestyle, work restrictions, culture or social expectations make it difficult to adopt the grazing approach, so you may have to compromise, perhaps by eating snacks of fruit between meals, for example.

Avoid eating large amounts at one sitting or eating lots of sugary snacks as this can cause drastic fluctuations in blood sugar levels. Eating habits that encourage these large fluctuations can be a factor in diabetes. Don't skip breakfast and expect your body to be able to magically find energy from somewhere. After several hours of sleep in which your body has been repairing and regenerating you, it needs sustenance. Breakfast may be the most important meal of the day so choose healthy, nourishing food to start your day. If you don't eat breakfast, your body will probably compensate by functioning on a lower intake, although it is unlikely to be working at optimum efficiency.

Beware of processed and prepared foods, even those from supermarket ranges that imply they are healthy. Many processed foods have lost much of their nutritional value and often include harmful additives and sugar. Artificial flavourings, colourings and preservatives can cause allergies and other adverse reactions. Many people attribute the recent huge increase in diabetes to the inadequacies of our modern convenience diet, and especially the addition of so much sugar to processed foods. Some processed foods contain more sugar and salt in a single portion than dieticians recommend we eat in a week or even a month!

Many fizzy drinks have a very high sugar content, so minimise your consumption of these if possible. A typical can of soft drink contains enough refined sugar to suppress your immune system for hours. If you drink several of these throughout the day, you run the risk of decreased immunity all day long.

Note that many sugar-free drinks contain artificial sweeteners, which also have a detrimental effect. Aspartame contains many toxins, and breaks down within the body to form formaldehyde, which is a neurotoxin. There are many diseases associated with aspartame toxicity, including neurological damage, cancers and eye problems. However, because the toxins are absorbed by tissues throughout the body, the symptoms can be diverse. Ironically, aspartame causes carbohydrate cravings, so if you are using it to cut down on your calorie intake, you may find yourself actually eating more. Perhaps you could consider researching the effects of artificial sweeteners in health publications or via the internet. The evidence I found was strong enough to persuade me never to eat or drink anything containing artificial sweeteners. Even non-diet fizzy drinks often contain some artificial sweeteners along with the sugar, so these are best avoided.

Most soft drinks also have high concentrations of phosphorous. The phosphorus binds to calcium, a mineral vital for normal bodily functioning. If your body cannot access the calcium it has extracted from your food, it has to find it from somewhere else, usually your bones or teeth. This could increase your risk of dental problems, bone fractures and osteoporosis in later life.

If the idea of cutting out fizzy drinks sounds too difficult for you, you have a decision to make. Assess the rest of your diet and consider your total intake of sugar and artificial sweeteners. Is there a history of diabetes or obesity in your family that might make you more susceptible to the effects of excess sugar? Is osteoporosis a risk factor for you? Are the potentially devastating effects of too much sugar or sweetener worth the enjoyment of the drinks?

High-fructose corn syrup (HFCS) is being used in an increasing number of products to add sweetness. It is a sweetener derived from corn that manufacturers use because it is cheaper than sugar. It is often used in products that claim to be 'health foods', despite the fact that it is highly processed and treated with genetically modified enzymes. Many people, even some doctors, believe that as fructose comes from fruit, it must be healthier than sugar. This may be true in small quantities and in its natural form, but HFCS is far from natural. Fructose has to be metabolised in the liver, unlike glucose, which can be metabolised by every cell in the body. Diets high in fructose can have a destructive effect on the liver. Although eating fruit is beneficial to health, large amounts of additional fructose can be hidden in processed foods in the form of HFCS, so it is a good idea to check the ingredients of packaged foods.

Healthy lifestyle advice recommends reducing alcohol consumption. It even suggests the number of units you should limit yourself to in a week. Alcohol is a poison. It goes directly into the bloodstream and causes the ill effects you are probably familiar with. These effects are signals telling you that drinking alcohol is having a detrimental effect on you. Ignore them at your peril. A healthy body can usually cope with the adverse effects of alcohol and appears to cleanse the system in a few days.

However, it is likely that some toxins are left behind, having a cumulative, negative effect. For those who over-indulge and become alcoholics, their marvellous body adapts to the continual onslaught of poison and actually changes the chemical constitution of the liver to protect the vital organs and the rest of the body as best it can. The alcoholic body often manages to function for decades (although in a highly distressed state) despite being poisoned daily, until eventually the liver has been damaged too much and gives up.

Alcohol consumption is so accepted in our society that few people consider how unhealthy it is. We even have public houses where you can go and poison yourself with your friends! How did we arrive at this bizarre situation? Some people consider it a sign of strength to consume excessive amounts of alcohol. It seems that they feel they will be respected if they can poison themselves and live to tell the tale. It is ironic that the alcohol is probably destroying the strength that they are so keen to demonstrate.

If you don't want to cut down on drinking alcohol, drink slowly to make it last longer, and intersperse the alcoholic drink with glasses of water to reduce the dehydration caused by the alcohol. For ongoing support, give your body the best possible chance of recovery by drinking plenty of water and other pure fluids, following a healthy diet and taking regular exercise.

It was widely reported that red wine reduces the risk of heart disease. The reason for this is that the crushed grape seeds and skin are left in the wine for a few weeks during processing, allowing the release of antioxidants. Antioxidants help clean up the free radicals that can damage cell membranes, possibly leading to vascular disease. Some people use this information as an excuse to drink more wine. In moderation your body can probably cope, but remember the antioxidant properties come bundled in a poison. It seems to me a better option is to simply eat the grapes and other foods rich in antioxidants.

The dangers of smoking have been well known for decades and the diseases and conditions directly related to smoke inhalation are well publicised. In addition to these risks, the nicotine and other chemicals in tobacco interfere with the major functions of the body, inhibiting the proper absorption and utilisation of nutrients. Even with an exceptionally healthy diet it is almost impossible to maintain good health if you smoke. Inhaling the smoke from other people's tobacco products can have similar detrimental effects, as can other forms of airborne pollution.

A vegetarian diet is usually portrayed as healthy, and many vegetarians are very healthy. Animal products have a relatively high fat content, and high fat diets are linked to obesity and heart disease. Eating meat increases oestrogen levels in the body, and high oestrogen levels are a predominant factor in breast cancer. It is therefore preferable to keep your consumption of meat to a minimum. However, there are some nutrients that may only be available in meat or fish and to cut these completely from your diet may not be the best decision. A small amount of lean, preferably free-range meat or poultry may be a better option. If your tastes or morals prevent you from eating animal products, consider taking a supplement to provide the missing nutrients.

Unfortunately, most meat on general sale is likely to have come from animals who have been given antibiotics, hormones or feed that deviates from their natural diet. The stressful conditions leading up to slaughter may also cause animals to produce an excess of some hormones. Antibiotics, hormones and the waste products circulating in the animal's body at the time of death will be absorbed into its tissues. If you eat meat, you will ingest all these toxins.

There is speculation that the increase in mental conditions such as dementia and Alzheimer's disease is connected with a lack of essential fatty acids (EFAs), also called omega oils, in our diet. It may be that a lifelong lack of these essential fats affects the brain, resulting in mental illness. Some therapists have also linked a lack of EFAs with learning disabilities.

Consumption of oily fish, the main source of EFAs, is reducing, and the average diet in the UK is now deficient in these nutrients. EFAs are required for healthy brain function. However, the Food Standards Agency has warned that those who eat more than two portions of oily fish per week could be at risk of ingesting an excess of harmful industrial pollutants and mercury that are in rivers and seas. This is another dilemma. One option is to take a liquid supplement of non-fish based omega oils, which is primarily flax seed oil. You will have to decide what is best for you. There does not seem to be an easy way of detecting if you are deficient in EFAs, but any family history of mental illness may help you make an informed decision.

Whole foods are better than processed foods. Processing often removes vital nutrients, especially when skins or husks are removed. The fibre in the whole food is beneficial to the digestive system and helps maintain healthy bowels. Choose wholemeal bread, brown rice and whole wheat products rather than the white alternatives.

Make your diet varied and balanced. You may be congratulating yourself for replacing the chips you used to eat every day with a baked potato. This was probably a positive change as there are several advantages of a baked potato over chips. Much of the goodness in a potato is in and just below the skin, and the skin itself provides beneficial fibre. So a baked potato that retains the skin is a healthier option in this respect than chips made from peeled potatoes. Chips are fried in oil, which has a high fat content, so a potato baked without oil is preferable. However, recent research suggests that baking may produce the chemical acrylamide, which can cause cancer. At the time of writing, this research is incomplete, but the point is that if you choose a variety of alternatives to chips, any negative effects attributed to a specific food or method of preparation are likely to be reduced.

Do not think that taking supplements is a substitute for a healthy diet. In foods, nutrients are found in combinations that work together for maximum benefit and are just right for our digestive systems. Your digestive system is very complex and starts with chewing. Chewing produces saliva and allows the stomach to prepare for the arrival of foods. The stomach acids are perfectly balanced to extract the goodness from the food, and the actual bulk of the food aids the digestive process. A tablet taken in isolation may not be properly processed, and therefore the nutrients may not be absorbed. Some of the caking agents in tablets or gelatine in capsules may also affect the absorption process. If your digestive system is not functioning healthily, it is unlikely that you will receive the full benefit of the supplements you are taking.

Some people may argue that intensive farming and overuse of pesticides have stripped the soil of much of its nutritional value, and therefore many foods are nutritionally deficient. They say that taking artificial supplements is the only way to get certain nutrients. If you believe this to be true, you may want to experiment with supplements in addition to your balanced diet and monitor the effect. If you notice benefits from the supplements, then you may decide to continue to take them.

Many of the fruits and vegetables we buy from our supermarkets are picked before they are ripe, so have a reduced level of antioxidants. If you have access to fresh farm produce that is not harvested early, then choose this whenever possible. If not, supplementing with antioxidants may be a sensible precaution. But do not use this as an excuse to eat fewer portions of fruit and vegetables. They contain many other vital nutrients that are essential to your health.

Be aware that it is possible to overdose on supplements, so always ensure you are taking a safe dose. Some mega-dose supplements contain amounts of the elements that it would be impossible to get from foods in such a short time. Some excesses are expelled from the body, for example, an excess of vitamin C can cause diarrhoea, but others can be damaging or even dangerous. Synthetic vitamin D is particularly toxic if taken in excess.

When you are considering supplements or natural remedies, make sure you find impartial information. The product advertising is almost certain to make claims that the product in question will improve your health in some way or other. It may include scientific sounding 'evidence' and technical jargon to help convince you. And just because it is labelled 'natural' or 'organic', does not mean it is safe. Personally I am all in favour of natural remedies and I sometimes use them myself. However, the natural remedies, supplements and complementary therapists who may prescribe such solutions have very limited regulation. Take responsibility and do your own research. See Chapter Ten for more information on this subject.

Recently, a flyer was delivered through my letterbox claiming a new method of losing weight. It said 'no exercise, no restriction on foods, no special diet'. I didn't investigate this any further, but I inferred that you could carry on abusing your body with junk food and slouching around, yet appear slim and healthy. (I may be wrong about this particular method, but I'll use the idea as an example.) If such a method works, and of course there were testimonials from people who had used it successfully, it suggests to me it is another way of ignoring your body's messages. An excess of fat is a clear message from your body that you are not looking after it properly. It is almost certainly a reflection of poor diet and lifestyle. Anything that masks this response could have serious consequences for your future health.

If you are unsuccessfully trying to lose weight and think you are eating a healthy, low-calorie diet, be aware that fat cells store toxins. If your body was not eliminating all the toxins you were ingesting, they may have been stored in the fat cells, among other places. Your marvellous body recognises this, and judges if it could handle the release of these toxins. If it decides they would overload your system and possibly make you ill, it may prevent the fat cells from being released to protect you, so you don't lose the fat. A possible solution to this is to drink plenty of water to help eliminate the toxins and to take antioxidants, especially vitamin C. Antioxidants break down the free radicals created by excesses of fats and sugars.

Your body requires time to digest the food you eat and extract the nutrients from it. If you eat a large meal in the evening, you may not be able to digest it all before going to bed. If you go to sleep before the digestion process is complete, the food will probably be laid down as fat. Sumo wrestlers use this principle to help them create the bulk that is advantageous for their sport. They eat a large (although healthy) meal, then go to sleep. So unless you want to be that shape, don't eat anything substantial for the last four hours of the day.

The low-carbohydrate diet for weight-loss has received publicity recently. The idea is that you can eat as much fat as you like, while restricting your carbohydrate intake (eg. breads, grains, starchy vegetables). The body is then forced to get its energy by breaking down stored fat. Be very, very cautious about this, and only embark on it if you fully understand all the implications. Personally, I do not agree with this approach because of the excessive stress it puts on the body and the potential lack of nutrients from restricting high-carbohydrate foods. I believe that a balanced, natural, whole food diet coupled with exercise will enable the vast majority of people to achieve and maintain a healthy weight.

Most healthy eating advice recommends cutting down on fat intake. However, your body needs some fat, especially EFAs. Much of the advice offered a few years ago about cholesterol has now been proven to be wrong. Only about 20 per cent of people who suffer heart attacks are found to have high cholesterol, indicating it is not so much of a threat as originally thought. People who have been taking cholesterol-lowering drugs for many years are now starting to suffer with heart problems from the drugs.

Hydrogenated and partially hydrogenated fats are definitely to be avoided. They have no known nutritional benefits, but if eaten to excess can cause coronary heart disease. They are formed when cooking fats at high temperatures, such as during frying. Check the ingredients lists of the packaged foods you eat. You may be surprised at how many of them contain hydrogenated fats. Avoid them whenever possible, although it may be impossible to avoid them completely as they are used so freely in many packaged foods.

I encourage you to take your diet seriously, but it is worth putting the issue into perspective. You need food to survive, and limiting your range of foods may leave you deficient in some nutrients. The risk of driving to the shops to buy a high-fat meal is probably greater than the risks associated with eating that one meal. And worrying about the nutritional content of everything you eat may have a negative effect on your health, as discussed in part two. Use your common sense to reach a sensible balance.

Preparing and cooking your own meals has the advantage that you can use fresher ingredients and you know exactly what is going into the recipe. Usually, preparing your own meals is cheaper than buying ready-made alternatives and need not be too time-consuming. Support your body by finding and following the diet that is healthy for you. Do further research into nutrition if you think you need to. Remember, your health is your responsibility.

Chapter 4

Sunlight

Sunlight is essential for life on this planet and always has been. But now, suddenly, it has apparently become dangerous. We are told that the hole in the ozone layer means that harmful ultraviolet (UV) light is no longer being filtered out, so we are more at risk from these allegedly harmful rays. The widely publicised advice is to keep out of the sun because it is reported to cause skin cancer (melanoma), cataracts and premature ageing. Unfortunately, this advice is misleading and could damage your health.

It is relatively easy to perform a study, produce a set of statistics and infer from them results that are wrong or misleading. Researchers who are looking for a certain result can usually manipulate the statistics to support their hypothesis, overlooking many other possible interpretations. For example, let's consider a group of people in Africa who live outside and are exposed to strong sunlight, but have no access to sunglasses. They apparently develop more cataracts than the rest of the population, so the scientific conclusion was that sunlight was the cause of the cataracts. The fact that these people are chronically malnourished was conveniently ignored.

Stressed laboratory animals who have drops put in their eyes to paralyse them and their eyelids pinned back before having UV light shined into their eyes for days at a time are hardly a representative sample. Their natural defences of looking away, reducing their pupil size and dropping their eyelids have been inhibited. However, such techniques have been used, and the results extrapolated unrealistically to make assumptions about the effects of sunlight on the eyes of humans.

Full spectrum natural light, which includes UV, is necessary for normal body functioning. The pineal gland controls the rhythms and cycles that regulate our bodily functions, especially the secretion of the tiny quantities of hormones that are required to maintain the delicate balance of all our systems. This regulation requires sunlight to work properly. Therefore, lack of sunlight can disrupt our natural processes, so is a health hazard. We all need sunlight to live healthily. If you spend most of your time indoors under artificial lighting, you are missing out on vital UV and it is likely your health will suffer to some extent.

Sunglasses have become a fashion accessory. We are told that we need to wear sunglasses to protect our eyes from the sun. I even see people wearing sunglasses on cloudy days and indoors! It is true that in exceptionally bright conditions, for example when sunlight is reflected off snow or water, sunglasses are a sensible precaution. However, for most conditions, the eyes are designed to cope perfectly well. In bright light the pupils will become smaller to reduce the amount of light entering the eyes. If it is still too bright, the eyelids will close a little for further protection.

Unfortunately, many people spend most of their time in artificial lighting conditions. Even the brightest light bulb doesn't come anywhere near to the brightness of the sun. Some people wear tinted glasses or contact lenses, which reduce the amount of light entering the eye. Even non-tinted eyewear cuts down light entering the eyes to a certain extent (compare the view through a closed window and an open window to prove this for yourself). Add to this the dirt, grease and dust that accumulate on glasses throughout the day, and it will be apparent that this represents a significant light reduction. Their eyes become desensitised to the intensity of natural light, and they find natural light too bright to tolerate, even on an overcast day. So they wear sunglasses to avoid the discomfort, which further desensitises their eyes to light.

The pupil contracts in response to bright light. The eye has evolved to expect full spectrum light, and UV is part of this. Wearing lenses prevents the UV from entering the eye, so some information that the visual system needs to decide how much to contract the pupil is lost. This means it may not contract enough to compensate for the lighting conditions, causing discomfort in bright light. The problem is the lenses, but the solution most people adopt is tinted lenses or sunglasses, which just perpetuates the problem and desensitises the eyes to light even more.

If your eyes are sensitive to light, gradually increase your exposure to brighter light to retrain them how to respond. If you wear glasses, take them off whenever you can safely cope without them. Spend more time outdoors. Avoid sunglasses whenever possible and wear a hat or eyeshade instead. This is a gradual process, be sensible – don't cause yourself any discomfort, and above all listen to your body and use your common sense. Never look directly into the sun. Your naked eyes will not allow you to do this; an automatic reflex will cause you to look away or close your eyes. Sunglasses will inhibit this reflex, but do not look directly into the sun even when wearing sunglasses.

Sunlight is good, so spend as much time outdoors as possible, even on cloudy days. The sun is still there when it is cloudy, and it is very beneficial to be outdoors even if the sun is behind the clouds. Do not allow yourself to burn, and spend time in the shade if necessary. Our skin has natural defences against the burning rays from the sun, and as long as you use simple common sense there is probably no need for 'protective' sun creams or lotions. In fact the sun 'protection' creams may carry more risks in themselves than the result of sun exposure.

You know your own skin-type best, and you may decide that you need some protection, at least at first. However, I recommend that if you have particularly fair or sensitive skin you stay in the shade, or build up the time you spend in the sun very gradually. Don't underestimate the strength of the summer midday sun. Our skin determines how to protect itself against the sun and how much melanin to produce by monitoring the brightness and the amount of UV entering the eye. If you wear sunglasses, you are inhibiting this process and are more likely to suffer from sunburn. I prefer a hat to shade my eyes and face.

If you rarely spend time in the sun, start by enjoying early morning or late evening sunlight. At other times, spend just a few minutes in direct sunlight and gradually increase your exposure over the following weeks. The unpredictability of the UK weather sometimes means that the first warm sunshine encouraging us to be outside does not arrive until May or June. The sun is at its most intense at the summer solstice on 21st June, so be very careful if your first sun exposure of the year is around this time. Skin that has been covered all winter will have less protection against the sun's rays. When sunlight is reflected off water or snow it increases your overall exposure, so be especially cautious in these circumstances.

There is more evidence that the increase in melanomas is caused by nutritional deficiencies and lack of vitamin D, than by increased exposure to sunlight. In fact, the group of people least likely to suffer from melanomas are those who work outdoors, so have higher than average exposure to the sun. Sunlight is our body's most important source of vitamin D. The European recommended daily allowance (RDA) of this vitamin assumes a certain amount of exposure to sunlight, so if you keep out of the sun you will need more of this than the RDA. However, you should know that artificial sources of vitamin D are toxic in high doses, so do not over-supplement on vitamin D.

Another possible reason for the apparent increase in the incidence of skin cancers is the cocktail of toxic chemicals we put on our skin daily. Most widely available soaps and shower gels contain chemicals that irritate, weaken and damage the skin. These are discussed in more detail in Chapter Six. These chemicals can react with each other to form carcinogens. They can also penetrate and build up in the eyes, interfering with the normal healing process, which may contribute to cataract formation.

Most people feel better on bright, sunny days, and I believe this is a natural response to life-giving sunshine. Some people become depressed in the winter when there are fewer hours of sunlight and the tendency is for more dull and rainy days, especially if they cannot get outside much. This has been recognised and named Seasonal Affective Disorder (SAD). Most sufferers find that spending an hour or two per day in front of a light box emitting full spectrum light relieves their symptoms. We instinctively like to spend time in the sun. No wonder most of us prefer to spend our holidays in sunny places.

I believe many of the ailments and illnesses that seem to be becoming more common nowadays can be attributed to some degree to lack of sunlight. Vitamin D3 is known to be effective in inhibiting the growth of tumours, and UV is essential to the synthesis of D3 in the body. Even obesity, which is becoming more prevalent, could be related to lack of sunlight. UV stimulates the thyroid, increasing metabolism and therefore helping weight loss. There has been much attention given recently to the Mediterranean diet as it is allegedly very healthy. However, could the state of health of the Mediterranean people also be related to the fact that they have more sun exposure than we do in the UK?

Vitamin D is required for calcium absorption. If your body cannot extract enough calcium from the foods you eat, it will take it from the bones. Therefore, inadequate intake of vitamin D (or inadequate exposure to sunlight) has the potential to cause osteoporosis and increase your susceptibility to fractures. Your marvellous body may compensate by growing spurs and bony deposits to limit movement in an attempt to protect against activities that could result in fractures and deformities to the weakened skeleton.

One of the effects of exposure to sunlight is that it causes free radicals to be formed. Some diseases and wrinkling of the skin are attributed to free radicals. Some people therefore draw the conclusion that we should keep out of the sun. However, free radicals are formed from our body's own functions, and are essential to extract energy from our food, so, as you might expect, your marvellous body has a mechanism to clean them up. A healthy diet consisting of plenty of fruit and vegetables, especially brightly coloured ones, should provide enough antioxidants to neutralise the free radicals. And plenty of water will help rehydrate your body and skin. Chemicals, drugs, some fats from meat, pollution, tobacco smoke and alcohol are also sources of free radicals; all the more reason to avoid these if possible. There really is no substitute for a healthy diet and lifestyle.

Enjoy the sun and use your common sense. I believe that time outdoors and moderate and sensible exposure to sunlight are part of a healthy lifestyle. If this is really not possible for you, consider the use of full-spectrum lighting.

Chapter 5

Exercise and Movement

Human beings are designed to be active and a moderate amount of exercise is good for us. It promotes the functioning of all our bodily systems, increases circulation and helps deliver vital oxygen throughout our body. Load bearing exercise such as running increases bone density, which helps to protect against osteoporosis. Our marvellous body even encourages us to exercise by producing endorphins that make us feel good.

Health and fitness are not the same thing; you don't necessarily have to be fit to be healthy. Indeed, athletes who train to the peak of fitness often find themselves more susceptible to health problems because they push their bodies to the limit and leave nothing in reserve to fight illness. However, sensible exercising contributes to overall physical health, and increases oxygen to the brain, which can help with mental alertness.

It is recommended that we take a minimum of thirty minutes' exercise at least three times a week. Motivation is an important part of your exercise regime. I believe that the more fun your regular exercise sessions are, the more likely you are to continue with them. If you have to force yourself to go to a gym to ride on a cycle machine, run on a treadmill or lift weights, you may often conveniently find you have more important things to do. Find a form of exercise you enjoy and look forward to.

If you choose sports that involve other people, you have a commitment to them to show up as arranged. (Strangely, I have found that many people are more likely to keep a commitment to others than to themselves.) If this isn't possible, setting personal targets may help to motivate you. Be clear about your goals and choose an exercise that will help you achieve them. For example, if your goal is to lose some weight, and you decide you will take regular cycle rides with a friend, stopping en route for a pub lunch and a few beers, this is unlikely to support your goal. You may still derive benefit from the exercise, but to lose weight you probably also need to address your diet.

Make sure you have the right equipment for your chosen sport to protect your body and avoid injury. Jogging puts a great deal of strain on the joints. If you go jogging, invest in a well-fitting, supportive and shock-absorbing pair of trainers. They are not likely to be cheap, but if you aren't willing to spend the money on them, your body will probably pay the price many times over in pain and injury. If you cycle, make sure your bike is the correct size for you. If you play racquet sports, ensure the racquet is the appropriate weight for you and the handle is the right size. I strongly recommend you visit a specialist in your chosen sport for the best advice.

Use your common sense when it comes to exercise and respect your body. If you feel especially fatigued, perhaps it is a message to miss this exercise session and rest instead. If you feel pain in a certain part of your body after exercise, your technique may be causing excessive strain that may lead to injury. Do what you can to understand and respect your body and recognise that pain is a signal that something is wrong and needs attention. Notice the difference between mild muscle aches that disappear a few days after exercise, and chronic aches and sharp pains that may be signs of strain.

If you are training for competitive events it is best to have a training plan. There are many aspects of a good training plan, including hydration, nutrition, strength, stamina, recovery time and psychology. A good coach should be able to provide the necessary information. Even if you are just training for a fun run or similar event, you should be aware of how to get the best from your training. Your muscles need fuel and fluids, so make sure you are drinking plenty of water and eating a balanced diet that includes adequate carbohydrates. Make sure you are fully hydrated before exercise and take on fluids during the activity and afterwards. You need energy before exercise, and then to replace what has been lost as soon after finishing as possible. In some circumstances you may need fuel during the activity.

I know some people go jogging before breakfast. All their energy reserves are used up maintaining and regenerating their body while they are sleeping, then they go out with empty energy banks and wonder why they can't run very far. They force themselves to continue, so the body has to find the energy from the muscles, the same muscles that the person is trying to train. They find they make little progress in their training programme.

Even if your goal is to lose weight, it is better to eat breakfast before exercising to get maximum benefit from the session. If you exercise before eating, you are demanding energy when none is available. This creates an emergency situation for your body, so it finds the energy from the most quickly and easily accessible source, which is the muscles, as it takes more time to metabolise the energy stored as fat. You may still lose weight, but the weight will most likely come from the muscles rather than stored fat. You may then appear thin but saggy, rather than having the slim, toned look you were probably aiming for.

Your body needs time to recover after activity, and overtraining can be self-defeating. Use your common sense and give yourself sufficient recovery time between sessions. Sleep is an important part of recovery, as this is when your body regenerates itself.

Exercise produces lactic acid, and if your exercise sessions are particularly long or intense, this may become trapped in the muscles. Drinking plenty of pure fluids will help this lactic acid to disperse, and I recommend massage to help the muscles recover. Exercise also causes free radicals to be formed, so you should take antioxidants afterwards, which are found in most fruits and vegetables and especially those that are dark red. You may also want to consider taking an antioxidant supplement.

Exercise does not have to be gruelling to be effective. Half an hour of brisk walking can be beneficial, especially if this is outdoors in fresh air. Gentle exercises such as yoga or Pilates that work on a subtle level are also beneficial. In general, the more flexible your muscles and ligaments are, the less likely you are to injure yourself. Always warm up and stretch sufficiently before exercise, and warm down properly afterwards. If you exercise outdoors or in a cold environment, wear sufficient clothing to keep the muscles warm.

Without regular exercise, fitness can diminish to the extent that your system becomes sluggish. This may be a gradual process so that you don't realise how it has affected your well-being. If you feel exhausted at the end of the day despite not doing anything physically demanding, this is probably a signal that you need to increase your activity levels.

If you have no desire or opportunity to take exercise at all, at least make the effort to include some activity in your routine. Technology makes it easy to lead a sedentary life, but there are alternatives. For example, take the stairs instead of the lift or escalator, stand up or walk around while talking on the telephone, walk down the corridor to your colleague's office rather than telephoning or sending email, walk or cycle to the shop to buy your newspaper.

Even when you are not exercising, many of your muscles are active. Just sitting requires some muscles to be engaged to keep you balanced and upright, and of course your heart, lungs and other internal organs continue to function. Your skeleton is a delicately balanced structure, and the body compensates where possible to keep the integrity of the structure.

If you habitually lean your head to one side, you place a strain on the vertebrae in your neck. These will gradually wear unevenly and probably cause neck problems later in life. The imbalance in your head will most likely be transmitted to your spine, shoulders, pelvis and legs, and your whole body will become unbalanced. Imbalances can cause pressure on nerves and strain on joints and muscles that can lead to pain and disruption of internal processes. Your posture is very important.

Be aware of how you normally sit, stand and walk. Ideally you should sit straight, with your back straight and supported in the lumbar region, and your feet flat on the floor. The average sofa does not provide adequate lumbar support and encourages poor posture. Habitually crossing your legs, slumping, or leaning forward will cause strain which may lead to imbalances. Even sitting on a wallet in the back pocket can eventually cause pelvic imbalance.

If you work at a desk, keep your shoulders relaxed and level if possible. Arrange your work so your neck does not have to strain downwards or forwards. Do not strain your neck by holding the telephone between your ear and shoulder. Avoid exposing one part of your body to draughts or a different temperature from the rest. Have all your equipment within easy reach so you do not have to twist or strain to reach anything. I cringe when I see the way supermarket check-out operators normally twist and strain to perform their duties.

When you are standing, keep your body relaxed and straight and your feet slightly apart. Imagine you are suspended from a cord attached to your head at the crown. This will help you keep your neck straight and your shoulders relaxed. Avoid the temptation to put all your weight on one leg, as this puts a strain on one side of the body. Allow your arms to relax by your side if possible. Alignment of the spine is key, so pay special attention to this.

High-heeled shoes cause your weight to be distributed in an unnatural way. Your body will probably compensate by tipping your pelvis, which can cause severe imbalance throughout your skeleton and contribute to conception, pregnancy and birth problems for women. Any ill-fitting shoes can distort and damage the structure of your feet so that your base support is compromised. This can transmit distortion and imbalance throughout your body. Is the perceived glamour really worth the pain and health problems these fashion accessories can create?

Hold your body in a relaxed way when you walk. If you are carrying something, balance the weight as much as possible. Bags held in one hand or over one shoulder encourage the shoulders to tilt, and this imbalance will affect the neck and spine. A rucksack or bum bag is preferable to a bag carried to one side. The most efficient way to carry loads with the least strain on the skeleton is on the head, but this is a little impractical and not generally accepted in our society. When lifting heavy items, bend your legs and keep your back straight rather than bending from the waist.

In everything you do, especially things you do frequently, notice if you are holding tension in your body. For example, check your driving position, your posture while working and the way you sit while watching television. Your position while eating is important; sit straight and relaxed without compressing your abdomen to allow your digestion to work effectively, and don't tense your shoulders.

Your marvellous body will compensate for any chronic tension as best it can. This may avoid discomfort in the short term, but could lead to serious problems in the long term. For example, a man who suffered a severe pain in his back that was diagnosed as a slipped disc said "I only bent down to tie my shoelaces." He did not realise that the damage was done to his vertebra over years of poor posture and neglect of his body, and that this incident just happened to trigger the emergency.

Most of us are unbalanced to a certain extent because one side of our body is dominant, but this will not necessarily create problems for us. Many sports encourage one-sided development of muscles, so it is often useful to include a variety of activities that exercise different muscles. This may also help to reduce imbalances caused by some muscle groups being much stronger than others, which can pull the skeleton out of alignment. Existing structural alignment problems may require the intervention of a bodywork practitioner.

Posture is also a factor in effective breathing. Correct breathing comes from the abdomen. When you breathe in, allow your abdomen to rise first, then your chest. If you compress your abdomen with poor posture or sitting for extended periods, you may inhibit full breathing and decrease the amount of oxygen getting to your body and your brain. If you work at a desk, standing up and moving around often helps your ability to think clearly, especially if you take the opportunity for deep abdominal breathing. Full, deep breathing also helps with relaxation as it stimulates the parasympathetic nervous system.

Making regular exercise and good posture a habit will support your body and contribute to your general health and well-being. To a certain extent, regular exercise can help to compensate for a less than ideal diet and lifestyle. I'm not suggesting you use this as an excuse to over-indulge often, but the perfect lifestyle is almost impossible in our current society, so exercise should be considered an important requirement for health.

Chapter 6

Skin

The skin is the largest organ of the body. It performs many important functions, including protection of internal organs, regulation of body temperature and the formation of vitamin D. It contains all the sensory nerve endings that are essential for touch and pain. If it is damaged, it repairs itself automatically, usually so perfectly that there is no evidence of the injury. Most of us take for granted the wonderful elasticity of the skin that allows the muscles and joints underneath a wide range of movement.

Your skin is covered with pores that allow oils and fluids to leave the body. Although the skin is generally waterproof, it is possible for some fluids to be absorbed through the pores, and moisturising creams rely on this principle. Fluids that are absorbed into your skin can make their way into the bloodstream and be transported around your body. As proof of this you could try rubbing a clove of garlic onto the soles of your feet. After a few minutes you will be able to taste the garlic and the smell will be on your breath.

It is a sensible precaution to wear gloves when you use household cleaners. Many kitchen and bathroom cleansing products contain harsh chemicals that could be absorbed through the skin. Some warn against using them on certain surfaces but rarely mention the skin. If they can damage plastics, for example, think about the effect on your body! Washing your hands after contact with these cleaners, even for a short time, may not be enough to completely remove the chemicals. Even washing powders can irritate the skin, so use a very small amount. I believe the manufacturers' recommended quantities are excessive, and adequate cleaning can be obtained from a quarter of that amount or less. Synthetic fabrics and the dye in clothes can also cause skin reactions. I prefer my clothes to be made from natural fibres.

In some situations it can be useful for fluids that are applied to the skin to be absorbed. Aromatherapy massage relies on the essential oils being absorbed and allowing the circulatory system to take them to the part of the body where they can be of benefit. It is useful to be able to rub cream into dry hands, although rehydrating from inside by drinking plenty of water is preferable. But there are some substances that you probably consider to be safe that actually may have harmful effects if absorbed.

If you use cosmetics, examine the list of ingredients. Most make-up products, skin cleansers, moisturisers, tonics and lipsticks contain chemicals. Anti-perspirants contain aluminium. Ask yourself if you would swallow these substances. If the answer is no, then you should not allow them to be in contact with your skin.

Make-up is usually on the skin for hours at a time, and cleansers are rubbed in, forcing some of the fluid and make-up into the pores. There are plenty of opportunities for these chemicals to enter your body's vital systems. Some people spend most of their time with these harmful chemicals on their skin. Not only are they ingesting chemicals, but by blocking the pores with these products, they are also inhibiting one of their body's natural elimination mechanisms, making it more difficult for the chemicals to be expelled.

Eye make-up can easily smear and enter the eye, either when touching your eyes or from the moisture and tear fluid. Irritation to the sensitive tissues in and around the eyes, caused by cosmetics, may encourage you to touch your eyes more. Every blink and movement of the eyes distributes the fluid, potentially allowing a small amount of the cosmetic into your body through the eye.

Read the ingredients list on the soaps, shower gel or bath foam you regularly use. These also have the potential to be absorbed, especially as you probably use them with hot water, which encourages the pores to open up. You rub them onto your skin and soak in them. Most bath and shower products contain sodium laureth sulphate, sodium lauryl sulphate and propylene glycol. These are for creating lather or thickening and serve no purpose in cleansing. They are hazardous chemicals that require special handling procedures and breathing apparatus when used in industrial locations. When you get soap into your eyes it stings. The irritation is your body warning you that these are dangerous chemicals.

Some people are particularly sensitive to these chemicals and develop allergies. They may be lucky enough to identify the source of the allergy, but often the role of personal care products is overlooked. If you think these chemicals may be contributing to an allergy or condition, you may want to use the muscle testing technique from kinesiology described in Chapter Three. For others the effects are more subtle, gradually poisoning the body, compromising and damaging long-term health. For people who already suffer from poor health, the burden of these chemicals can be too much for the body to cope with and can contribute to a further decline in body functioning.

I can understand the appeal of shower gels. They produce lots of lather and feel smooth on the skin. This may make you think that they are getting you clean and conditioning your skin. When you realise that the pleasant texture comes from the main ingredient of brake fluid and antifreeze, you may modify your opinion!

You may think that it is safer to use products designed for babies. Think again – they often contain the same harmful ingredients and are even more of a potential danger to babies as their skins are thinner and their immune systems are immature and less able to deal with the toxins. Even specialist infant products such as baby wipes are loaded with chemicals. They may make life easier for you, but they may well cause health problems for your child.

Shampoo is basically the same as shower gel and also contains a similar list of harmful chemicals. Sodium lauryl sulphate actually inhibits hair growth – great for washing your hair with! We massage the shampoo and its chemicals into the scalp, all around the areas in contact with the brain. Some probably enters the ears and possibly the eyes. We bombard our bodies with these chemicals daily. Note there is no benefit from shampooing twice as the directions sometimes advise, except to the manufacturer's profits.

Consider the other hair care products you may use. If you use hair dye, you may find it odd that you have to wear gloves to protect your hands from the chemicals, yet they are apparently safe to be in contact with your head for twenty minutes. Have you noticed how carefully hairdressers handle these chemicals? Look at the instructions on how to deal with spillages or accidental ingestion. To me these give a clear message that the products are not suitable to be in contact with the skin at all. Indeed, hair dyes have been linked with bladder cancer. Hairsprays that stick your hair in a certain position must surely also stick to and block the pores in your head. This will interfere with the natural oils in the follicles and probably undermine the health and shine of your hair. There is a very strong possibility that it will even inhibit hair growth.

The irony is that most cosmetics and personal care products are designed to enhance your appearance, but they are more likely to have a negative effect on your appearance in the long term. The cosmetics industry is a huge money-spinner. Manufacturers aren't concerned if one of the products they sell causes your hair to look dull and lifeless, or even fall out, because then they can sell you one of their vast array of products that claim to revitalise or thicken your hair. If their lipstick results in you losing the natural colour from your lips, they can probably count on you being a lifelong customer. And who promotes the image of beauty that demands so many different products to create it? The cosmetics industry of course.

Attempts to highlight the dangers of such commonly used products are often thwarted by the misguided opinion that as the majority of the population uses these products daily, they must be safe. Using these products is such an automatic part of our daily routine that few people consider it could be risky. Many people believe that the government would not allow the sale of potentially dangerous products. They conclude that most people use them and are apparently still healthy, but the fact is that general health is declining and the incidence of serious and degenerative disease is rising.

Sometimes the body of evidence forces an investigation into the safety of certain chemicals or substances. Some chemicals are now used in quite different products and circumstances from those for which their original licence was granted. Experiments and surveys are conducted, and the conclusion is usually that there is no significant health risk as long as the directions for use are followed.

My response to this is that firstly, there is usually some ambiguity about the amount of the product that is recommended to be used. 'Squeeze a small amount of liquid...' is open to interpretation. Perhaps the amount that was determined to be 'safe' to use is considerably smaller than the average handful that most people use. Secondly, the source of the research is rarely made clear, if mentioned at all. The research may have been carried out by eminent scientists from XYZ laboratory, but the chances are that it was funded by the cosmetics industry itself. It is likely that the industry took the parts of the report that reflected favourably on its products and discarded the rest. Statistics can usually be manipulated to show the results the industry wants to present. The quarter of a million people who may be adversely affected are not statistically significant.

I find it quite sad that so many people feel the need to cover up or alter their appearance in the name of beauty. Cosmetic surgery is becoming more common and available to more and more people. Men and women are having implants, injections, tucks and liposuction to make them feel more attractive. I recently saw a newspaper photograph of a famous actress wearing a bikini. The editorial said how fabulous she still looked, despite being over forty years of age. It went on to describe the many surgical procedures she had undergone to achieve this look. I realised that I was not looking at her beauty, but at the artwork of her cosmetic surgeon. I could not see the real person. I feel the same way about make-up; it is not real, it is made up, it hides the real person.

Injections, implants and surgical procedures carry an element of risk, but evidently some people believe it is worth it, to create the appearance they want. I understand that changing aspects of themselves can make some people feel more confident, but that is not addressing the real issue. The real issue is that they do not accept themselves as they are. Self-acceptance is an important part of your health and well-being. If you feel the need to resort to cosmetics or surgery, ask yourself what it is you are trying to hide from. You may find the techniques described in part two of this book helpful in recognising your true beauty.

Interestingly, the words 'health' and 'beauty' are usually used together. Apparently we instinctively realise that a healthy body and mind radiates beauty. A healthy diet and lifestyle are an excellent way to sustain natural beauty. Healthy skin, shiny hair, bright eyes and a trim, firm figure come from a balanced, healthy diet and lifestyle. Unfortunately, medical science and technology provide ways that may seem to create beauty from the outside with little personal effort, but we all know that beauty really comes from within. Applying a mask to the skin, or changing the shape or texture of it with surgical techniques does not change the person underneath, and as we have explored, may cause damage to the person's health, which will eventually be reflected in the skin.

Many people touch their face excessively throughout the day without being consciously aware of it, perhaps as a nervous reaction or just through habit. The natural oils in the hands and fingers pick up dirt from the objects we touch, and as we use our hands extensively in everyday life, they come into contact with many other things. If you touch your face, you transfer some of that dirt to the skin. This can contribute to spots, pimples and blocked pores. If you touch your eyes, mouth, nose or ears, any bacteria or viruses you have picked up (and these are lurking everywhere) have a high probability of making their way into your body.

Ask a friend to discreetly count the number of times you touch your face in a ten minute period, for example. You may be astounded by the answer. Start to be aware of when you scratch your face, rest your chin in your hand, rub your eyes, brush your hair from your face, touch your forehead or stroke your chin while contemplating, for example. Aim to minimise contact between your hands and face, and when you catch yourself doing it, congratulate yourself. Scratching irritated skin is often a major factor in the perpetuation of rashes, and is usually done without realising.

There are products for use on the skin that do not contain harmful chemicals, but you may have to go to health stores or special outlets to buy them. Check the labels very carefully for undesirable chemicals. Some products may be branded as natural or organic, but this may mean that just one or two of the ingredients comply with this claim. Even aromatherapy or other products made up by a therapist are most likely to be made from a standard, chemical-laden base.

Truly natural and safe products may be more expensive than popular supermarket brands – the harmful chemicals are used because they are cheap and add bulk. If you switch to natural products you will probably need to use much less, and because they are not so harsh on your skin, you may not need conditioners and moisturisers, therefore saving money overall.

Body brushing with a soft-bristled brush is an excellent way to tone your skin. Start at your feet and use small strokes to brush towards the heart. Brush your legs, arms and back in this way. I find about seven strokes on each area is adequate. Body brushing improves the circulation of blood and lymphatic fluid, which benefits your whole body, including your skin.

If you feel that the risk of using chemical-laden products is acceptable, you could consider using smaller amounts than you do currently, to reduce the risk. Remember that these chemicals may build up in your body over many years, and the effects may not be evident until the damage is irreversible.

Chapter 7

Eyesight

Our eyesight is our most acute sense and the mechanics of visual perception are the most complex of all the senses. The eyes are actually an extension of the brain. The information that enters your eye has to be interpreted and converted into images that you can understand. It is an incredible process that most people take for granted. But the number of people with visual problems has now reached epidemic proportions.

We are encouraged to look after our eyesight by having regular eye tests with an optician. Opticians believe that the eye is like a camera, that the shape of the eyeball is fixed, and that errors of refraction such as short- and long-sightedness cannot be reversed. They apparently believe that the marvellous self-regulating and self-healing properties that apply to all other organs and systems of the body are absent from the visual system. They think that vision is a purely physical process and unaffected by the mind. These beliefs couldn't be further from the truth.

The eye is a living organ with sensitive tissues and cells that can be affected by chemical and hormonal changes in the body. Vision fluctuates throughout the day in response to what is happening in your body and is affected by your general health and well-being. For example, most people recognise that their vision is often not as sharp when they are tired. The process of seeing occurs mainly in the mind, so your mental and emotional state can be at least as important as the physical in your visual health.

If you visit an optician because your vision is blurred or disturbed, it is almost certain that he or she will recommend glasses or lenses for you. Your general health or your level of stress will probably not be considered. You will not be advised how to correct your eyesight or how to protect it from further deterioration. You will be fitted with a pair of glasses or lenses that appear to make things look clearer. They feel a bit strange, and everything distorts as you move your head, but the optician assures you that 'you'll get used to it'.

If you wear these glasses they start to interfere with correct visual functioning. The prescription you are given matches the state of your eyes at the time of testing and takes no account of normal fluctuations. The glasses fix your eyes at this diminished level of visual functioning and inhibit your body's natural tendency to heal itself. Glasses and lenses don't correct the visual impairment, they encourage it, and if the conditions that caused the problem in the first place are not removed, the glasses will probably cause further deterioration in your eyesight (this is explained in more detail later in this chapter).

This is great news for the opticians because it means you become one of their lifelong customers requiring new eyewear regularly. And if they can persuade you that you need the latest designer range, a spare pair, contact lenses for sport, coloured contact lenses for vanity, and perhaps a pair of prescription sunglasses too, their income from you increases even more.

I should point out that there is a group of opticians called behavioural optometrists who may use prescription glasses in conjunction with relaxation and other techniques to improve vision. The glasses they prescribe are usually weaker than a conventional optician would prescribe, in order to give the visual process a chance to correct itself. In this case, these glasses are a temporary step towards clear vision.

People who are short-sighted can see things that are close, but distant objects appear blurred. Short sight is usually caused by excessive close work that can cause a strain on the eye muscles. If you engage in a lot of close work for long periods each day, you are working the muscles hard. As with all muscles, excessive use, especially under stress, leads to strengthening and shortening of the fibres, and this is true of the eyes. This shortening of the muscles can eventually distort the eyeball, causing myopia.

The glasses prescribed for the myopic person are designed to allow them to see at a distance of six metres or more. Focussing at this distance is considered to be very similar to focussing at infinity, at which the eye muscles are most relaxed.

If you wear these glasses all the time, your eyes are always under strain and never able to relax. If you wear them for close work, you place an even greater strain on your eyes when they try to accommodate to the short distance. The eyes often compensate in the same way they did previously, which is to shorten the muscles even more. This results in a greater degree of myopia, and this downward spiral is termed progressive myopia.

If you strained any other muscle of the body, you might expect a doctor to prescribe some sort of temporary physical support, such as a bandage or brace, and perhaps some physiotherapy consisting of exercises to restore full strength and flexibility to the damaged area. You would not expect to be fitted with a permanent cast or calliper that weakened the muscle, and those surrounding it, even more. Yet this is exactly what opticians do when they fit you with artificial lenses.

Not only do glasses contribute to progressive myopia (and may be the sole cause), they cause strain on the whole visual system. Pressure in the eyeball can be affected, which can lead to glaucoma. The strain on the elongated eyeball to accommodate close up while wearing prescription lenses can result in detached retina. Wearing contact lenses reduces the supply of oxygen to the eye and interferes with the natural lubrication. There is a high probability that people who wear contact lenses every day will get an eye infection at some time.

People who are long-sighted may be able to see things in the distance clearly, but cannot see close objects. Presbyopia is the condition that often affects older people and is caused by hardening of the lens so it is unable to change shape enough to see close up. This is not an inevitable part of ageing as opticians will tell you, but usually a result of poor diet and lifestyle. Toxins and sugars can build up in the lenses, interfering with their elasticity and even causing cataracts. A detoxification programme can often reverse presbyopia and clouding of the lenses in a few weeks.

Hyperopia is the condition of long-sight where the eyeball is too short from front to back, so the hyperope cannot see clearly at any distance. This can be caused by poor diet and lifestyle as above, but it is becoming more and more common in younger people. One reason for this is that opticians have started prescribing lenses for long-sight for very young children.

It takes a long time for the visual system to strengthen and mature enough to learn to focus correctly, just as it takes a long time to learn the co-ordination required for other motor functions like walking, running and catching a ball. With the rapid growth and changes taking place in an infant's body, and particularly the head, it may take a few years for vision to completely settle down. Left to their own devices, most children will develop normal sight and be able to focus clearly at all distances, especially when they start learning to read.

However, if opticians can get in quickly and diagnose long-sight before the infant's visual system is fully developed, they can prescribe glasses and prevent the child's vision from learning to focus properly. They can start them off on their lifelong reliance on glasses even before they start school. What an excellent scheme for the profits of opticians. How are they allowed to get away with it?

Eye tests for our children are often organised by their school. The child enters the darkness of the optician's examination room for a test. It is quite likely that the child may be a little anxious about this, perhaps scared of the dark and worrying if she will pass the test. She is placed in an unfamiliar chair and has a large, heavy piece of apparatus placed on her face. She is asked to read as far down the chart as she can. If she cannot read the bottom line, does she think she has failed the test? The point is that the conditions of the test can set up stress that will affect the visual process and impair her ability to read the chart.

The test usually consists of being given two lenses to compare. You have to say which lens makes the eye chart look clearer. What if neither gives clear vision? You have to pick one. All the time the eye is looking through an artificial lens, normal focussing is being disrupted. By the time you have looked through half a dozen different lenses, your eyes and brain may be quite confused and producing errors of refraction in an attempt to compensate. Even if there is little wrong with your sight, you may still end up being prescribed glasses, as happened to me at the age of nine.

If you wear glasses, you do get used to them, just as the optician promised. You get used to the distortion of images, you ignore the headaches. If you are long-sighted you learn to leave a bit more room around you because you have realised that the zoom effect of your glasses means you can't see things immediately to the side. You accept and no longer notice the discomfort on your nose and ears, and when the glasses slip down your nose, you push them up automatically, without being consciously aware of it. You don't notice that looking through the lenses dulls colours, especially as the dust and grease builds up on the glasses. You get used to the restriction the frames have placed on your field of vision. You tolerate the glare and reflections the lenses create. You accept that when you walk into areas with a large temperature or humidity change, or when you sweat, your glasses will steam up and you won't be able to see at all.

If you wear contact lenses you quickly learn to ignore the irritation they cause in your eyes. You get used to the dryness and the awkwardness of inserting and removing them. You accept that sometimes something will get stuck behind one of the lenses causing discomfort and possibly permanent damage. You accept or ignore the risk of eye infection that could lead to blindness.

Over time, your eyes learn that there is only one tiny area of the artificial lens that gives clear vision. They learn to minimise their movement so they tend to look through this point more. The natural movement of the eyes is impaired and they begin to stare. Often you move your head more to compensate, leading to neck ache, which can restrict the optic nerve and impair the vision even more. Staring causes the rapid, minute eye movements called saccades, that are vital for clear vision, to slow down, further diminishing your ability to see clearly, even through glasses. The artificial lens scatters light onto areas of the retina outside the fovea centralis; the tiny area that gives the greatest visual acuity, so you are unable to see detail clearly. Now you can't see clearly even with your glasses and there are no artificial lenses that can compensate for this situation.

Usually, the longer artificial lenses are worn, the more strain builds up in the visual system. Most people find their prescription changes over time, often including extra complications such as astigmatism. Astigmatism is where the muscles around the eyeball pull unevenly, distorting the shape of the eye in a plane other than the horizontal. This can be caused by neck tension, habitually tilting your head, reading at an angle or lying down, or working with a light source that casts light unevenly on the work surface.

If you wear lenses all the time, you limit the amount and quality of light entering your eyes. This can interfere with the correct functioning of the pineal gland and ultimately affect all systems of the body. The longer you wear lenses, the more likely it is that the disruption of the pineal will cause hormonal imbalances throughout your body, possibly compromising your health.

The constant strain of wearing artificial lenses can cause neck tension and tight shoulders. This chronic tension can cause imbalances in the entire skeletal system, which can lead to serious health problems as described in Chapter Five.

Some people, often particularly stubborn individuals (like myself), and especially children, find that glasses interfere and are completely incompatible with their lifestyle. They are unwilling to persevere until they 'get used to them' and they refuse to wear them. These people often find that their sight improves naturally, or they didn't need glasses anyway. When an optician is presented with this information, the most likely response is that the initial diagnosis was wrong. They are very unlikely to accept that there was spontaneous recovery because it does not fit in with their training.

Most people trust their optician, so when they are told that visual deterioration is inevitable, or that it is hereditary, they tend to believe them. Although it is true that there are genetic factors that can affect eyesight, hereditary errors of refraction are extremely rare. However, a child of parents with visual defects may well mimic the poor habits of seeing from its parents. Children pick up many subtle signs from their parents, and these can include fixed gaze, reduced saccadic movements, infrequent blinking and neck tension, all symptoms of poor visual functioning.

What makes the situation worse is that it has been known for over a hundred years that glasses are harmful, cause visual deterioration and affect overall health. Dr Bates designed and practised a holistic system of relaxation and techniques to restore perfect vision naturally. He recognised the role of the mind and imagination in the perceptual process, and he realised that stress can have a negative effect on vision. He highlighted the inadequacies of conventional optometry, but his theories were never accepted by mainstream medicine. Perhaps opticians were already too greedy for our lifelong dependence on their products to admit the truth.

Wearing artificial lenses can be hazardous to your health in many ways. Problems with focussing or other visual problems are a signal from your body that something is wrong. The opticians' solution is to mask the symptoms at the expense of your vision and your long-term health. Laser treatment also masks the symptoms and has a whole host of other complications associated with it. Double vision, ghosting, scarring and permanent damage to the cornea are just some of the possible side-effects. And of course, if your visual system has been diminished by years of wearing artificial lenses as described above, merely burning off a bit of the cornea to correct the refractive error will not restore perfect vision.

Normal vision is relaxed and easy, defective vision is associated with strain. If you have visual defects and you want to improve your vision, I encourage you to investigate the Bates method of natural eyesight improvement, the concepts of which are described briefly below.

The first thing you should do is remove your glasses whenever you can do so without posing a danger to yourself or others. If your vision is particularly poor, you may need to get a weaker prescription as an interim step. The most important aspect of naturally perfect vision is relaxation. Dr Bates advocated cupping the hands over closed eyelids while resting your elbows on a table. Do this whenever your eyes feel tired and ensure your shoulders and neck are relaxed.

Full, abdominal breathing is important to deliver adequate oxygen to the eyes, and frequent blinking helps refresh them and replenish the cleansing and lubricating fluids. Alter your focus frequently by looking up from close work, for example. Allow your eyes and the muscles around the eyes, and in the neck and shoulders to relax. Keep your eyes active by watching things in motion such as trees in the wind, birds or a bouncing ball.

It is a common mistake for people with diminished vision to try and see everything in their field of vision at once. There is one tiny point on the retina that gives the best visual acuity; everything in the periphery is less sharp. Therefore, to achieve good vision you must look at just one point at a time. Allow your eyes to move over the object, noticing the detail at each point. Your brain will then create a clear image of the complete object in your imagination.

Your imagination plays an important role in vision because your brain has to create the image from previous experiences. It takes longer to make out unfamiliar objects, or objects in unlikely surroundings. For example, if you look into a tree and see a black object, your first assumption is likely to be that it is a blackbird. Scanning the detail may however reveal it is a sock that has blown off a nearby washing line.

Modern technology puts particular demands on the visual system. The flicker from fluorescent lights, televisions and computer screens can interfere with the saccadic movements. VDUs place a strain on the eyes and can blur vision, despite official assurances to the contrary.

If you spend a lot of time in front of a VDU, don't sit too close to it, and look away into the distance frequently to avoid fixing your focus. Attend to your position and posture so that your whole body and particularly your neck and shoulders can be as relaxed as possible at all times. Angle the screen so that it is below your eye level and you cannot see reflections or glare. Lower the brightness as much as possible – the radiated light from a VDU stresses the eyes more than reflected light from a page of paper. Use a small font to encourage small movements, as a large font encourages the eyes to make big jumps which may disrupt the saccadic movements. The radiated heat and light can dry the eyes quickly, so blink frequently to keep them relaxed and moist.

A healthy diet and lifestyle coupled with exercise supports natural, clear vision. Essential fatty acids are required for brain and eye function, and refined carbohydrates are known to be detrimental to the eyes. Free radicals can be particularly damaging; all the more reason to eat plenty of fresh fruit and vegetables for their antioxidant properties. The supplements grape seed extract and bilberry are thought to be especially beneficial to eye health. Exercise helps deliver vital oxygen to the eyes, and the movement encourages eye mobility.

Mental strain can cause visual problems, so you may find some of the relaxation techniques in part two of this book helpful to improve your eyesight.

Perhaps you feel that you have worn artificial lenses for so long that there is no hope for you. This is not the case. People who have worn glasses for decades have restored their sight and improved their overall health in the process, using Dr Bates' methods. They have discovered that there is much more to vision than just being able to see black letters on a white background six metres away. Most people who practise this technique report that everything seems brighter and more distinct, their colour perception is enhanced and they can see much more detail than they could when wearing their lenses.

If you are comfortable with your artificial lenses and not interested in improving your vision, just be aware that there are risks associated with that decision as described above and in Chapter Four, and that you may be compromising your health. Many people happily wear glasses all their life without severe health problems, and the choice is yours.

Chapter 8

Teeth

As well as contributing to a pleasant smile, a healthy set of teeth allows you to bite and chew. In this respect, teeth can be considered as part of the digestive process. We need them to work properly to grind up food into a size we can swallow, and to allow the saliva to start to break down the foodstuffs, ready for the stomach enzymes and acids to process. Chewing your food sufficiently is therefore an important part of successful digestion. Eat slowly to give your stomach time to act on the food and to avoid indigestion.

Dental care and maintenance programmes are an accepted part of our routine. We brush our teeth once or twice a day, many of us visit a dentist regularly for a check-up, and some people floss and use mouthwash. I can't think of a more successful healthcare programme in terms of acceptance by such a high percentage of the population. I believe one of the reasons it is so successful is that it gives us personal responsibility. It has been drummed into us that if we brush our teeth regularly and visit a dentist for check-ups, cleaning or hygiene, there is a high probability that our teeth will serve us well throughout our lives. We understand it is up to us and we are willing to invest the time and effort to look after our teeth.

Perhaps another element is that poor oral health contributes to bad breath, and advertisers have warned us how unpleasant this can be and that even our best friend would not tell us if we had halitosis. Therefore, we had all better use their products to avoid such embarrassment. Vanity may also be an issue, as neglected teeth can be unsightly. I think the personal commitment to dental care is a remarkable achievement, and it is unfortunate that there is not the same emphasis on other aspects of our health. Under normal circumstances, many people devote more time and effort attending to their dental health than they do to the rest of their body.

Some of the work performed by dentists is good. For

example, straight teeth not only look good, but they are less likely to trap food than misaligned teeth. Food trapped between the teeth for prolonged periods can erode the enamel and may contribute to dental caries (decay). If the teeth in the top and bottom jaws do not line up properly the chewing mechanism may be less effective and digestion may be affected. Dentists can correct such misalignments. Plaque removal can be beneficial to dental health as well as improving the look of your teeth. Dentists can spot the signs of gum disease and other problems that could lead to lost teeth, among other things. Note that smoking reduces the circulation in the mouth and can mask gum problems.

Unfortunately, not everything the dentist may do is so positive. I believe that routine polishing of the teeth is best avoided. You might think whiter teeth look good, but polishing may damage the enamel, and the high-speed electrical polishing instruments can cause vibrations throughout your mouth. These vibrations may cause tiny cracks that could allow bacteria to enter, possibly resulting in dental caries. I recommend having your teeth cleaned only when it is necessary for health purposes rather than just for cosmetic reasons.

If your dentist discovers you have an area of dental caries, he or she will almost certainly drill out the decayed part of the tooth (using a high-speed drill that may well create more cracks) and fill it up with highly toxic mercury. Most dentists will assure you that the mercury amalgam is stable, but the truth is that the mercury can leach out into the mouth and be absorbed into your body. Mercury poisoning has a negative effect on the immune system and is thought to be a factor in ME, MS, some allergies and Alzheimer's disease.

If you think your mercury fillings could be contributing to poor health, you can go to a specialist dentist and be tested. The specialist will also be able to remove the fillings if they are found to be causing you problems, and replace them with a safer, non-toxic compound. Note that the safe removal of mercury fillings requires great care and should only be performed by someone specifically qualified in the specialised technique. Some, but not all, holistic dentists are qualified in this area.

Several years ago a health report suggested that for adults with healthy teeth, one check-up a year would be sufficient. It also said that small areas of dental caries should not necessarily always be filled and may even go away of their own accord. Of course, the report was criticised by the dental profession as irresponsible and negative. Use your common sense and your awareness of your teeth and your family's dental health to decide when to visit your dentist.

The best way to look after your teeth is to eat a healthy diet and brush gently twice a day using 'correct' brushing technique. Ideas about optimum brushing style seem to change periodically, so check with your dentist or hygienist. Most dentists also recommend flossing to clean between the teeth where a toothbrush may not reach. If you use dental floss, take care to be gentle so as not to damage your gums.

Avoid sugary snacks that can get stuck in your teeth as this provides a fertile breeding ground for bacteria. Sugars can react with the bacteria in the mouth causing plaque. Plaque sticks to the teeth and gums, and the warmth and moisture inside the mouth allow the bacteria in the plaque to multiply, which can lead to tooth decay. The more times you eat during the day, especially high carbohydrate foods, the more opportunities you provide for the bacteria to breed, increasing the risk of decay.

Don't think that eating foods with a high sugar content and then immediately brushing away the sugar is a solution. The reaction between the sugars and the bacteria begins within a minute of eating, so your teeth are most vulnerable from when you start eating, during the meal and for about twenty minutes afterwards. It would therefore seem to make more sense to brush your teeth before eating in order to minimise the bacteria present in your mouth for the sugars to react with. Also, sugar and the resulting acidity can soften the enamel, so vigorous brushing just after eating or drinking something sugary may damage the enamel, thus possibly doing more harm than good.

If you have children, encourage them to practise good oral hygiene and take care of their teeth from an early age. My mother did not allow me to have sweets as a child because she wanted me to avoid the problems and pain she had suffered with her teeth. You may think this sounds extreme, some may consider it unnecessarily restrictive or even cruel. But I did not feel at all deprived; in fact I enjoyed the experience of having pocket money to spend when all my friends had immediately spent all theirs on sweets. I was pleased that I never had to have any dental work done and felt sorry for my friends when they had to repeatedly go through the trauma of fillings and extractions. I am now deeply grateful that I have excellent teeth, and believe that avoiding sweets and sugary snacks has also contributed to my good health.

Most people don't consider what is in the toothpaste they use. Most widely available toothpastes contain harmful and even poisonous chemicals such as sodium lauryl sulphate and sodium fluoride. Mouthwashes also contain hazardous chemicals. There are safe alternatives, but check the ingredients carefully because even herbal toothpastes and those marked 'natural' may contain chemicals. If you cannot find a suitable alternative or decide to continue with your current brand, use a tiny amount and make sure you don't swallow any.

These harmful chemicals are also in children's toothpastes, and children younger than six years are less able to completely spit out toothpaste, so are more at risk of ingesting them. Also, the toxins may cause more of a strain on their immature immune systems. Some toothpastes are especially flavoured to encourage children to use them, but it seems to me that this may result in them using more toothpaste or swallowing it deliberately, posing even more of a threat.

Most toothpaste contains the toxin fluoride which claims to 'fight decay'. This is because at one time it was thought that fluoride hardened the teeth. Recent research has now reversed this theory and has established that although small amounts applied directly to the teeth may help to harden tooth enamel, ingested fluoride actually softens the structure of bones and teeth and does more harm than good.

For some reason, the medical profession and the government want to cling on to the idea that fluoride benefits the teeth. Study after study has shown the dangers of fluoride, but they are either ignored, or the data is manipulated to disregard the effects that are detrimental to health.

High fluoride intake is associated with increased risk of bone breakage, decreased immune function, increased risk of breast cancer and Alzheimer's disease, among other things. It interferes with the pineal gland and the production of melatonin, upsetting the delicate balance of the hormones. It has been noticed that the onset of puberty is earlier in children who live in areas with fluoridated water as a result of this imbalance. Mental disorders and syndromes such as attention deficit disorder have been attributed to excess fluoride, as have low IQ and increased violence.

Some fluoride may be absorbed while using toothpaste, even if you think you are spitting it all out. It may not be possible for the body to expel all the toxins, so they gradually build up, potentially causing health issues. When taken in relatively low doses, it can take up to twenty years for the fluoride to build up to a level that can cause health problems.

One way to help rid the body of toxic fluoride is to drink plenty of water. However, in some areas there is a high natural fluoride content, or fluoride is added to the water in the misguided belief that it is a good way to improve dental health. I advocate drinking plenty of water, but if your local supply is fluoridated I recommend drinking filtered or bottled water for the reasons outlined below. Standard filters may not remove fluoride, so you may have to investigate alternatives that do. Mineral water may also contain fluoride, so check the list of ingredients.

If you use fluoridated water in cooking, some of the fluoride may be absorbed into the food. Excess fluoride places a particular strain on the kidneys, so anyone with kidney problems should be especially careful. Diabetics are also more vulnerable to the toxic effects of excess fluoride absorption, as are those with thyroid problems. Some countries now accept the harmful effects of fluoride and systematically remove it from their water supply.

Fluoride reacts with the aluminium in cookware producing aluminium fluoride, which can be absorbed by the body relatively easily. In contrast, aluminium alone is very difficult to absorb. High concentrations of aluminium are implicated in Alzheimer's disease and other mental conditions.

The devastating effects of excess fluoride can be seen in Nalgonda, India, where tens of thousands of people are crippled, blind or have mental disorders caused by the naturally occurring fluoride in their water supply. In the UK, fluoride occurs naturally in varying amounts in water and some foods, so most people ingest a small amount. Tea contains high concentrations of fluoride, so if you drink a lot of tea you may be absorbing a dangerous dose. If it is made with fluoridated water, the risk increases substantially.

At the time of writing, the UK Government is considering fluoridation of the water supply in an attempt to address the poor dental health of a minute proportion of the population. If this happened in your area it would mean that every time you washed yourself, prepared a drink with water and cooked food in water you would be exposing yourself to a hazardous substance. Even if your local supply is not fluoridated, you may be drinking beverages prepared in fluoridated areas or eating food contaminated with fluoride because it has entered the food chain.

The UK Government's proposal is not to use naturally occurring fluoride, but industrial waste from the fertiliser industry; hexafluorisillcic acid. This toxic waste is contaminated with other poisons, including lead, mercury, silicon and arsenic. This is a hazardous waste that requires special procedures for its disposal. It is too toxic to dispose of in the sea, yet the plan is to add it to our drinking water! The potential for serious health problems from these toxic substances being added to our water supply is immense.

This proposal for compulsory mass medication breaches human rights and would mean that we can't even rely on the cleanliness and safety of our tap water. It seems to me that it is a step backwards to the days when contaminated water was a major factor in many diseases. A much more sensible (and cheaper) solution would be to teach healthy eating habits, including avoiding fizzy drinks, and correct brushing technique to the vulnerable few.

Fluoride supplements should also be avoided. These

contain sodium fluoride, which is eighty times more poisonous than the naturally occurring calcium fluoride. They can cause discolouration of the teeth from fluorosis, which is caused by a change in the normal chemical structure of the tooth enamel, making it more brittle than normal enamel. There is no conclusive evidence that taking these supplements reduces cavities. Some countries have banned fluoride supplements as they are so detrimental to health. A much better way to maintain healthy teeth is to eat a healthy, balanced diet.

There is mounting evidence that fluoride accumulates in the skeletal system, and can cause serious health problems, including osteoporosis. The mottled effect of teeth that is an indication of dental fluorosis is probably the only visible sign of fluoride poisoning. By the time the teeth are affected in this way, considerable amounts of fluoride are likely to have been incorporated into the bones, weakening them and making them more brittle.

Damage to the skeletal system caused by fluoride is irreversible. However, the healthier and more varied your diet is, the better your chances of eliminating excess fluoride that is ingested. Avoid artificial sources of fluoride and don't drink excessive amounts of grape or apple juice, which are particularly high in fluorides. This is especially relevant if you have diabetes, under-active thyroid (hypothyroidism) or renal problems. Calcium-rich foods help the body to rid itself of harmful fluoride, so ensure you have an adequate intake of calcium.

The jaw is part of the structure of the skull. Nerves from the body travel up to the brain in close proximity to the back of the jaw. Any misalignment of the jaw may interfere with the nerves and could result in health problems such as headaches, sinus problems, insomnia and breathing difficulties. Irregular teeth can cause jaw misalignment, as can extractions.

Wisdom teeth provide essential support for the temporomandibular joint just in front of the ears, yet dentists often routinely extract them, saying they serve no purpose. Without the support of the wisdom teeth, hearing could be impaired. But as the body is a finely balanced structure, problems with the jaw can cause a chain reaction throughout the whole body. These range from neck, back and limb pain to conditions as diverse as ME, irritable bowel syndrome (IBS) and mental illness. If you began to suffer ill health after dental extractions, especially removal of your wisdom teeth, you may want to investigate cranio-dental procedures to correct any misalignment.

Keeping a full complement of healthy teeth can form an important part of your overall health. Find a dentist you can trust. Discuss all the issues that concern you in advance, before you have a mouthful of instruments. If you do not feel comfortable with your dentist, find another. It may only take one filling or one extraction for your health to be affected. Unlike most systems of the body, teeth don't repair themselves, so you only have one chance with your adult teeth.

Chapter 9

Health Promotion Programmes

Prevention is better than cure and it is sensible to lead a healthy lifestyle to avoid illness. Health promotion or health awareness programmes seem like an excellent idea and some have been quite successful. Unfortunately, some schemes that are good in principle can be flawed, and we have already explored some of the negative aspects of dental and optical programmes and sun exposure information. The most successful schemes tend to be those that inform the general public and put the responsibility on the individual to act on the advice. Healthy eating campaigns are a good example of this type of programme.

It may appear that the publicity about the dangers of smoking has the elements of being a good scheme, as it informs and then relies on personal action. However, things are not always what they seem. The sceptical among us may question why it took the UK Government so long to ban tobacco advertising, even though the detrimental effects of smoking had been known for decades. Advertisements glamorising smoking appeared on many advertising hoardings with a token message about the adverse effects at the bottom. 'Smoking kills' or 'smoking causes cancer' appeared in contradiction to the tone of the rest of the advert – it almost seemed to be issuing a challenge to the smoker.

One clue to this situation might be the amount of duty the UK Government collects from smokers. You may think that this is fair because if smokers are less healthy than non-smokers as statistics indicate, they will require more resources from the health service. So the tax they pay on their tobacco products goes towards their healthcare. That is a good theory until you examine the monetary amounts involved and discover that the tax collected from smokers is far in excess of the NHS budget. The government would be in serious financial difficulties if all smokers suddenly stopped their habit.

But what about the government funded television

commercials encouraging smokers to give up? It certainly gives the impression they are committed to helping smokers to quit. However, every commercial that I have seen shows a distressed smoker explaining how hard it is to stop, portraying the idea and reinforcing what seems to be the accepted opinion that giving up smoking is a struggle. Of course, the tobacco companies would like smokers to believe this, too. Beliefs are very powerful, as explained in part two. However, I know many people who have just decided to 'stop smoking' and succeeded on their own without any problems at all. In my hypnotherapy practice I helped many people to stop permanently in just one session.

Consider also the stop smoking help lines and clinics that allegedly assist people to stop smoking. All the ones I have investigated recommend and supply nicotine replacement products which have a very low success rate and unpleasant, even dangerous, side-effects. This seems odd until you discover that the help lines and clinics are funded by the pharmaceutical companies that make these products. And why isn't hypnotherapy, the most successful intervention, promoted? Perhaps they realise its success would harm their income. I really have to question the sincerity of the 'stop smoking' programmes. If you are a smoker and you want to stop, your mind is your best ally and there are techniques described in part two that will be helpful.

Some health promotion schemes may be sincere but ill informed. Although regular testing may help to diagnose potential health problems, it might also result in people taking medication they may not necessarily need. The effect of high cholesterol levels was misunderstood, and now many people are suffering serious heart problems as a result of the medication they were prescribed. The risks associated with the medication can be greater than the risks of high cholesterol.

I have my personal doubts about some of the cases diagnosed as high blood pressure. We are all unique, and it seems likely that we all have our own optimum blood pressure level. I know several people who had no health problems but were put on blood pressure lowering pills after a routine test. I know that waiting around for hours in a hot, crowded doctor's surgery with lots of ill people and then having a tight collar squeezed around my arm makes my blood pressure rise! If this issue is relevant to you, remember that you know your body best. Be aware of symptoms that may be related to high blood pressure, the risks, your own health profile, and don't just blindly accept medication without reasonable cause or explanation. Take an active role in the situation and explore lifestyle changes that could reduce your blood pressure naturally (and more safely). If you think the test does not represent your normal state, ask to wear a 24-hour blood pressure monitor.

There has been a lot of emphasis on breast awareness recently in an attempt to lower the incidence of breast cancer. This would seem to be a positive step. Schemes that encourage regular self-examination are good because they create personal responsibility, and as individuals know their body best, they are the most qualified to detect any changes. However, programmes that invite women for regular mammograms and CAT scans may not be so positive. Radiation is known to cause cell mutation that can lead to cells becoming cancerous, and the screening machines emit radiation. So the machines designed to detect cancer cells may well be contributing to their formation or growth.

There is a certain amount of physical and mental trauma associated with the screening. The pressure put onto the breasts in order to produce a clear image can be painful and can rupture cysts and disseminate existing cancer cells. The stress and worry of the actual tests, of false positives and inconclusive results that mean the examinations need to be repeated can depress the immune system. Depressed immune function is accepted to be a factor in disease, including cancer.

There is so much concern about breast cancer that doctors are now helping women to discover if they have a high risk of developing the disease. They are even given the opportunity of having their breasts removed as a precaution! This is a typical example of the medical profession considering the body as an unrelated set of parts that can be treated in isolation. The doctor determines the level of risk largely based on genetic factors (looking at the family history) even though these are only relevant in about five per cent of cases. The most important factors are diet and lifestyle. Surely offering advice about lifestyle improvements, which can also contribute to overall improved health, is a better option than having healthy parts of the body surgically removed?

Women categorised as having a high risk of developing breast cancer are sometimes offered more frequent screening. This means their bodies are subjected to more radiation, more stress of the tests and more physical trauma; the factors that can increase the chances of breast cancer. Add this to the belief and expectation associated with being labelled as at higher than average risk, as explained in part two, and it becomes a self-fulfilling prophecy. Those in the high risk group do indeed develop breast cancer in a higher percentage of cases. The medical profession then uses this as evidence that the screening programmes are necessary, and the cycle continues.

The bad news is that the screening process is not reducing the number of deaths due to breast cancer. The same is true for the cervical smear programmes; there has been little change in the cervical cancer rate. Given that there are risks associated with screening, and that these may contribute to cancers, is screening beneficial? This is for you to decide. Weigh up the evidence, consider your own health, lifestyle and risk factors and make the decision that is best for you. Look for impartial information that can help you make the right choice.

Hormone Replacement Therapy has received a lot of publicity, and many people believe it is the answer to menopausal problems. Anything that interferes with the delicate balance of hormones in your body, such as HRT and the birth control pill, will disrupt normal functioning and could cause a wide range of health problems. There are well documented side-effects, such as ovarian cancer, breast cancer, blood clots and gallstones, but these are usually dismissed as insignificant. Do not accept HRT without fully understanding all the consequences. Remember that the powerful pharmaceutical companies will promote their products as safe in an attempt to make you their customer. The best way to protect your health through the menopause and beyond is to follow a healthy diet and lifestyle.

You have to put the risks in perspective. For example, there are risks associated with taking the birth control pill, and these are increased in certain situations such as being overweight, smoking and being aged over 35. Doesn't it seem a bit strange that the pill is apparently safe when you are 34, but not when you are 35? We are all unique and we age at different rates, so the limit seems rather arbitrary, yet it tends to be relied on by doctors and nurses. Pregnancy also carries risks, so if not taking the pill might result in pregnancy, you have to consider the implications. There are risks in everything we do, so with all these issues you have to decide which risks are acceptable and take appropriate action.

There has been much speculation about the safety of vaccinations, but we are usually assured they are all safe. However, there have been no long-term safety studies carried out, and any negative reactions are either not reported, or dismissed as coincidences or irrelevant. Diseases are injected into babies and their immature immune systems are expected to cope with it. Sometimes they receive many diseases at once. Yet when there are epidemics of these diseases, people who have been vaccinated contract the disease as well as those who haven't!

Some vaccinations contain a live virus. Could this cause the virus to spread? We know that widespread vaccination can cause a virus to mutate, thus posing a risk from new strains. In the first few days after being infected with a disease, the immune system is depressed, increasing the vulnerability to further infection. It seems likely to me that this risk is multiplied with combined vaccinations. Research into the safety of vaccines and other drugs is often carried out by the pharmaceutical companies who make them, so they have a vested interest in the results and how they are presented. Balanced, complete and unbiased information is very difficult to find.

For prospective parents, the health of their unborn baby is paramount and they do everything they can to ensure its health. Most mothers are given routine ultrasound examinations, yet ultrasound may cause subtle brain damage and has been linked to smaller babies, dyslexia and delayed speech. So what is the purpose of the examination? If abnormalities were detected in your unborn baby, would you terminate the pregnancy? What if abnormalities were indicated, but the aborted foetus was found to be normal? If the result of the examination would make no difference, you may want to consider if it is really necessary to subject your baby to a potentially harmful procedure.

The same goes for other foetal monitoring procedures. Chorionic villus sampling (CVS) can cause massive blood loss, endangering the foetus, and amniocentesis increases the chance of miscarriage. Sometimes the medical profession interferes using too many gadgets and procedures where nature copes very well on its own. At one time it was routine to X-ray babies in the womb to monitor their progress. Thankfully, the dangers have now been acknowledged, and the procedure has been discontinued. Make sure you understand the risks to you and your baby of any procedures before agreeing to them.

One problem with screening or visiting a doctor is that they like to diagnose a condition or disease and give it a name. As soon as it is given a name or label, (often just the symptoms translated into Latin), it becomes detached from you. It is something you have, rather than part of your body that hurts. Intellectually you realise you have control over something internal, but a condition with a label seems to become external, which gives the impression you have less control over it. Any disease is an imbalance of the whole, and the more you recognise this, the better your chances of regaining or retaining good health. This is discussed further in part two.

Unfortunately, orthodox medical practitioners are trained to accept that drugs, surgery or invasive techniques are the most effective ways of treating illness. In some cases, doctors are offered financial incentives to prescribe a particular drug. The pharmaceutical industry does its best to encourage the belief that drugs are the only way to 'attack' disease, and suggests that there are no alternatives. Few doctors are trained in nutritional therapy and few accept that diet and lifestyle changes can cure disease.

So be aware that some health promotion programmes may be motivated by factors other than your health. It may be pharmaceutical companies who want you to take their drugs, it may be political manipulation, it may be medical arrogance. Above all, remember that your health is your responsibility and do not agree to procedures you are not comfortable with. Don't worry about asking too many questions or being an 'awkward' patient. Patients more involved in their treatment plans react better and recover more fully than those who allow someone else to take control.

Chapter 10

Complementary Therapies

Complementary therapies have enjoyed an upsurge in popularity in recent years, even though many disciplines have been around for thousands of years. Many people are recognising that medical science does not have all the answers, and are unhappy with invasive procedures or the unpleasant side-effects of drugs. Most complementary therapies consider the mind, body and spirit as a whole, recognising that no part of the body can be treated in isolation. The therapies work in harmony with the body, allowing healing to occur in the most appropriate way for the individual. This is why they are called holistic therapies.

Holistic therapies should be seen as a way of promoting and maintaining good health. People who are used to conventional medicine that waits for disease and illness to occur before treating it may find this concept difficult to understand. The idea of visiting a complementary health practitioner when you are in good health may seem strange if you normally only visit a doctor when you are ill. This is a paradigm we must change. It is in your interest to take responsibility for maintaining your health, even if there is a financial cost. Of course, complementary therapies can also be effective to treat illness and conditions, but prevention is better than cure.

Orthodox medicine seeks to suppress symptoms with a quick fix rather than understanding their cause, whereas a holistic treatment addresses the whole person to create the conditions that will allow healing to occur naturally and fully. Holistic therapies acknowledge that we are all unique, and the treatment should be tailored to the individual. The orthodox approach of 'one drug fits all' apparently ignores our individual differences, affected by such things as age, body mass, gender, ethnic origin, and diet. Drugs can be absorbed very differently and have many different effects depending on metabolism, hormones, enzymes, blood proteins, body fat and other factors.

Part of the natural healing process promoted by

complementary therapies may be for chronic conditions to become acute before disappearing, which means that symptoms may become temporarily worse before they get better. Reactions may occur in other parts of the body because changes in one part affect the whole system. Reactions may also occur in the mind, such as dreams or emotional release, as the body and mind are intrinsically connected. These are issues that many people don't understand and they may discontinue their treatment, assuming it is not working or making the situation worse.

Given the completely different approach of holistic therapies from orthodox medicine, it is not surprising that many people disregard complementary therapies considering them to be fads or nonsense. Many of the concepts cannot currently be explained by science, so are discounted. Even theories that can be backed up by scientific evidence, such as photographing the meridians and aura, are rarely accepted by the scientific community. However, there is still a great deal of public support for complementary therapies. I believe one reason for this is that we instinctively have more faith in natural methods of treatment, or remedies that are made from natural sources.

Unfortunately, many therapies have become a victim of their own popularity. For example, homeopathy is a discipline where the remedy is carefully selected by the homeopath based on the characteristics of the person, or the way the person reacts to the presenting condition (or both). Several people with the same symptoms may be prescribed different remedies because they have different personalities, stature or skin texture. So to see a rack of homeopathic remedies lined up in a health store, each labelled for certain symptoms, is a misunderstanding of the therapy. Individuals may select a remedy, and if it doesn't clear their symptoms they may conclude that homeopathy is ineffective.

Aromatherapy is popular, and consequently the essential oils have become more widely available. As a result of high demand, some of the products on sale do not meet the requirements for collection and processing of true essential oils, and some may not even contain the oil! It is not always easy to determine which oils are of high quality, as many lower grade oils have the words 'pure' or 'natural' on the bottle. For all natural health products, it is best to go to a reputable supplier that has been recommended to you by an experienced therapist.

The high demand for some products has created instances of unethical and exploitative methods of collection. Some therapeutic ingredients are scarce, rare, or difficult to extract, but the financial gains of producing them can be compelling. Plant and animal species are under threat, as are certain habitats and cultures. Determining the ethics underpinning a particular product can be difficult, and even companies who claim to be caring or 'green' may be guilty of exploitation for profit. If you are interested in using complementary therapy products, I recommend visiting an experienced and qualified therapist. This is most likely to result in you receiving the right product for you, and one that is of high quality and ethically sound.

A concern about complementary therapists is that there is no enforced regulation or legal standards of practice. Demand for training in the vast range of therapies available has resulted in dilution of skills and a drop in teaching standards. Some therapists find that they cannot make a living from practising the therapy alone, so they go into teaching with little or no experience. This is unfortunate for the overall quality of the therapies offered and for the reputation of complementary therapies as a whole. So it is important to find a good therapist, preferably by recommendation from a trusted source.

I do not want to deter you from using complementary therapies, in fact I encourage you to use them where appropriate. I just want to make you aware that there are negative aspects so you can avoid them. You are more likely to be harmed by taking an aspirin than by a therapist or any complementary remedy, so safety isn't the issue. But if you choose a practitioner or remedy without being fully informed, you may not derive the maximum benefit. It is worth doing your own research to find the therapy that best suits you and to find a reputable practitioner. If you cannot get a personal recommendation, find an association or institute for the particular discipline. They will be able to give you information about the therapy and their accredited practitioners.

Just making the commitment to visit a complementary therapist is a positive step. It indicates you are taking responsibility for your health and you are willing to make the time and pay for the treatment (usually). Many therapies are pleasant to receive, and just allowing yourself time to relax and enjoy them, and talk to someone who will listen and give you their full attention, is beneficial in itself. It also sends a message to your mind and body that you are taking an active interest in your health. Many therapies encourage you to become more aware of your body, which is beneficial on many levels.

The aim of the majority of complementary therapies is to rebalance the energies of the body, mind and spirit. This may include lifestyle changes and some self-therapy between sessions, as well as the actual therapeutic intervention by the practitioner. You do not have to believe in the therapy for it to work, as proved by the fact that holistic therapies are successful on animals. You do have to have a willingness to participate in the therapeutic process and an openness to change. If you visit a practitioner with the sole intention of receiving a remedy to cure you, you are abdicating responsibility, and the results are likely to be less effective, or temporary.

Among the many diverse therapies available, it can be difficult to determine which one is best for you and your circumstances or condition. Some therapies are best suited to specific types of problem, such as the Alexander technique or the Feldenkrais method for postural correction. Be clear about what you want to achieve and research the therapies available for your intended outcome. If you feel curious about a particular therapy or drawn to it in some way, this may be the one for you.

As discussed in part two, your mental attitude is an important factor in your health. If you decide to use a holistic therapy, keep an open mind and engage fully in the treatment plan. If you are convinced it will be unsuccessful, you may block any improvements in your health and well-being, so maintain a positive attitude. You are more likely to derive benefit from a therapy that you enjoy and believe in.

Almost all complementary therapies cause subtle changes over a number of sessions, or from taking remedies or being exposed to certain stimuli over time. If you are the sort of person who likes instant feedback, you may be more comfortable choosing a therapy where positive benefits can usually be felt immediately, including various forms of massage and reflexology. These therapies have longer-term effects as well, but start working immediately to relax you and to remove toxins from your body. If you have a particular dislike of needles, acupuncture may not be your preference, although acupressure or shiatsu, which use finger pressure instead of needles to release energy blockages, may be an option for you.

If you are reassured by taking a remedy of some sort, homeopathy or Traditional Chinese Medicine may be suitable. If you believe environmental factors are related to your situation, you may consider Feng Shui or dowsing. Remember that only a small proportion of complementary therapists are medically trained, so they will not be able to diagnose illnesses or conditions, although they may refer you to a practitioner of another discipline if they feel it is appropriate. If you want a diagnosis or have severe or prolonged symptoms, it is your responsibility to consult a doctor or appropriate medical specialist.

I encourage you to explore complementary therapies. When you visit a therapist, ask for as much information about the therapy and its background as possible. Take an active role in your health and well-being. Be open to learning more about your body and be committed to the healing process.

Conclusion

The things that you eat, drink, inhale and rub on your body may seem harmless enough, but appearances can be deceptive. People have said to me that they believe if anything is harmful to us, it would not be allowed to be sold without health warnings. Unfortunately this is not always the case, which is why it is so important for you to be aware of the issues. Large companies are often more interested in profits than the health and well-being of their customers, and abuse their power to our detriment.

Products that offer us an easier or more convenient lifestyle tempt us to disregard some of our physical needs. Convenience, processed and prepared foods have quickly become the norm in most people's shopping baskets despite being nutritionally inferior. Coffee shops and fast-food outlets are multiplying. We are bombarded with a huge array of toxic personal care products. Tablets, medicines, spectacles, cosmetics and surgery can provide the illusion of health, at least in the short term. These issues may not necessarily pose a major threat to health individually, but the combined cumulative effect over many years may be too much for your marvellous body to cope with.

Things that contribute to our health such as life-giving sunlight and the therapeutic properties of natural medicines are portrayed as dangerous. The air we breathe has been polluted as a result of technological 'advancements' and there is a threat that our drinking water will be polluted with industrial waste. The medical profession, to whom we turn for support, does not always give us the best advice and often contributes to our ill-health through ignorance, arrogance or power.

Scientific research, a discipline that is relatively new to emerge, has taken precedence over common sense in many respects. If a scientific study can 'prove' something to be true, it is often accepted without question, even if it contradicts much of the evidence. Modern medicine seems to have replaced the knowledge and wisdom of natural healing accumulated over thousands of years. It has reduced the intricate complexities of the human body into disconnected parts that are treated like machines. It often does more harm than good.

Maintaining your physical health in our modern culture requires knowledge and commitment. Taking care of your body is your responsibility. I hope the information in part one will help you to make healthy choices and pursue the issues that are relevant to you in more depth. Remember that there are risks involved in everything you do, so the key is to find a sensible balance.

Part II

Your Mind

Chapter 11

Your Powerful Mind

In part one we discussed some of the marvellous automatic, involuntary processes that maintain your body and keep you healthy, such as breathing and digestion. As well as these instinctual processes, you have learned how to control your body to perform voluntary processes, such as walking. These are all functions of your incredibly powerful mind. Just think of all the other things you have learnt over the years. I don't necessarily mean your formal education, although you probably did learn many facts, theories, skills and methodologies during your schooling. Your mind is capable of so much, but most of us don't use it to anywhere near its full capacity. Let's consider just a few of the many complicated skills you have learnt, but probably don't give a second thought to.

You have mastered the complexities of language and can understand and converse with someone who speaks the same language, even if they have a different accent or tonality, speak quickly, slowly, monotonously, excitedly, or many other variations. You may not be able to explain the rules of syntax and grammar, or know what a past participle is, but you can still compose sentences with enough accuracy to be understood. Anyone who has studied the rules of a language will appreciate how impressive it is that we usually learn our native tongue without any formal instruction.

You can recognise a particular face from different angles, with different expressions, hairstyles, make-up, and even after the changes associated with decades of ageing. This skill is still too complex for us to fully understand, and attempts at programming computers in facial recognition have been largely unsuccessful. If you start to analyse the physical co-ordination required to play sports, the minute control and adjustment of the muscles, the balance, the timing, you will realise that this is also an incredibly complex feat.

You have the ability to recognise music, different melodies, voices and instruments. You can differentiate between performances of the same music by different artists, and probably discern any wrong notes. Your memory is so powerful that you can recall things you experienced as a child with perfect clarity. In fact we remember everything we have ever experienced, although we may not always be able to recall it at will. This is covered in more detail in Chapter Twenty. All these complex things you can do at the same time as your mind controls your breathing, heartbeat, circulation, digestion, hair growth and all the other functions that keep you alive and healthy.

So how does your mind achieve so much? There are many aspects of the mind that we still cannot explain. What we do know is that the mind consists of conscious and unconscious parts. Your conscious mind is your awareness and your thinking. It is logical and rational and does all your reasoning for you, helping you to make decisions. Things can go in and out of your conscious mind very quickly, but at any one time it can only deal with about seven pieces of information.

Your unconscious mind, by contrast, can deal with millions of pieces of information simultaneously. We have already mentioned the bodily functions that continue unconsciously. You have no need to be aware of these most of the time, so they do not enter your conscious mind. If there is a problem with any of these processes, the unconscious mind will alert the conscious mind, usually by producing pain or discomfort. This gives the best chance for conscious intervention to resolve the problem.

As well as internal processes, your unconscious mind is dealing with external stimuli. Your senses are bombarded with too much information for your conscious mind to absorb, so the unconscious mind filters out most of what is irrelevant at the time. You do not need to be aware of all the sounds around you; humming of various electrical devices, birds singing, people chattering, your own breathing, the paper as you turn the page, or whatever. But if the people chattering mention your name, that does have relevance to you, so your unconscious mind will immediately make you aware of it to allow you to listen to the conversation if you wish.

Similarly, you do not need to be aware of everything in your visual field. Your unconscious mind takes in every detail, but only passes things of relevance to your conscious mind. It determines what is relevant based on factors such as your personal safety, specific interests, preferences and recent events. While you are comfortable, it is not important for you to be aware of your back against the chair or your feet on the floor, and you probably weren't aware of them until reading this brought the sensations into your consciousness.

You have probably had the experience of setting out to do something but then being distracted. The distraction was your unconscious mind deciding to bring something else into your awareness. You can make a conscious choice not to follow the distraction, but you cannot prevent the unconscious mind presenting the distraction. Often, however, the distraction is strong enough to make you forget your original intention. If your unconscious mind decides that there is something that needs your urgent attention, it makes it very hard for you to ignore.

By now you may be beginning to realise that your unconscious mind controls a large proportion of your thoughts and actions. Many people will dispute that, saying that they are in conscious control and can choose what they think and do. Of course you can make conscious decisions. You may decide to reach for your drink, and that command will be sent to your unconscious mind and will usually be carried out successfully. But the exact muscle movements and balance required to allow you to do this are co-ordinated by your unconscious mind. You learnt how to perform them in infancy, and now they have become automatic, unconscious actions. So even many conscious decisions rely on unconscious co-operation.

The suggestion that we are not consciously in charge of our life can be quite threatening, which is why many people reject the idea. But we have already established that it is your unconscious mind that decides what information to pass into your conscious awareness, so it is clear that your unconscious mind directs the focus of your attention. This is a very important concept and one that you must accept if you are to use your mind more effectively and improve your health and happiness.

As we shall explore in the following chapters, all the decisions we believe to be consciously derived are influenced to some extent by our unconscious mind. It therefore makes sense to learn as much as possible about your unconscious mind, how it works, your motivations, beliefs and strategies. The more of your unconscious thought processes you can bring into conscious awareness, the more insight you will have. This will give you more options when making the decisions that affect your life.

Chapter 12

The Unconscious Mind

As explained in the previous chapter, you are controlled largely by your unconscious mind. The main purpose of your unconscious mind is to protect you, to keep you alive, healthy and comfortable. It is a survival mechanism that strives to keep you safe and to avoid anything that may threaten you. This is quite easy to understand on a physical level. For example, your immune system protects you from most of the germs and viruses that are present all around us. In the normal course of your life, any perceived external danger produces the 'fight or flight' reaction, so that you have the best chance of protecting yourself.

On a mental or emotional level, our unconscious strategies for protecting ourselves can sometimes be perplexing. You may wonder why a certain action causes you to be angry, yet a very similar one makes you sad. Or perhaps you have noticed that your determined efforts often fail, even though you believe you are totally committed to them. Understanding the nature of the unconscious mind may provide you with some insight into the reasons why you react in the way you do.

Memories are stored in the unconscious mind. Everything you have ever experienced is recorded. Your unconscious mind also records details that were not passed to your conscious mind. While you walk outside, you may be aware of a few sights and sounds around you, perhaps the temperature of the air and any unusual smells. You may be thinking about something unrelated to your environment. But your unconscious mind takes in and stores every detail of your surroundings. It remembers every sound, the colours of all the objects you pass, every change in the texture of the ground, even the number of strides you took!

I heard recently that in a survey of car drivers 80 per cent of people believed their driving ability was above average. This is ludicrous, of course, as only 49 per cent can be above average. I believe the reason for this misconception is that on each journey most people only notice the few drivers who make dangerous or inconsiderate manoeuvres and disregard the hundreds of safe drivers they see.

Things that are unimportant are not passed to your conscious mind, so you have memories you are not even aware of. There are techniques that can allow access to these memories, the most widely known of which is hypnosis. However, your unconscious mind will not release any memories if it believes doing so will cause you any problems, physical or emotional. Sometimes, a detail that did not enter your conscious mind at the time may be presented to you later. Some people describe this as a hunch. Perhaps it is an important piece of information, so your unconscious mind decides to make it available to you.

As part of its protection of you, your unconscious mind may repress certain memories. If you have suffered a traumatic ordeal or become very upset by a certain incident, the memory, or certain parts of the memory, may be kept hidden from your conscious mind. This is to protect you from emotional pain. Negative memories will normally be repressed until your unconscious mind believes you are emotionally mature enough to accept and resolve the issue on a conscious level.

The unconscious mind learns very quickly, so that anything you do repetitively becomes automatic. The first few times you do something, you have to make conscious decisions about how to achieve your aim. For your first visit to a new destination, you have to ask for directions or consult a map. Throughout your journey you have to be alert to make sure you take the right route and avoid any dangers that may be lurking in the unfamiliar environment. When you have successfully navigated the journey several times, it becomes committed to your unconscious mind and you can do it without thinking.

The same is true of any skill. The more times you practise it, the more automatic it becomes. Some activities become so habitual they require no conscious control at all. If you drive to work every morning, just getting in your car can be the trigger for your unconscious mind to take you to your place of work. How many times have you got into the car intending to go somewhere else, but found yourself on your journey to work? As we know, the conscious mind can only handle a few pieces of information at once, so being able to store and access common behaviours unconsciously has enormous advantages. This frees your conscious mind to think about more interesting things.

A cue or set of cues is required to trigger the memory. For example, the sight of a computer keyboard reminds you how to type, a few notes or words of a song bring the whole tune to mind; picking up a tennis racquet triggers the memory of how to play tennis. Once a skill or behaviour has become automatic, it will run whenever your unconscious mind receives the relevant triggers, until it is instructed by your conscious mind to stop. New memories and behaviours are constantly being added, often without your conscious awareness.

The capacity of the unconscious mind is too huge to comprehend, practically infinite. There is no possibility of the storage space being filled up, so millions of skills can become unconscious. The unconscious mind keeps them all available, with the most frequently and recently used ones more accessible. As the unconscious mind remembers everything, even skills and behaviours that have not been used for decades can be accessed. They may require a few more triggers and a little practice, but they do not need to be relearnt from scratch. The key to recall is using the right triggers, and this is discussed in Chapter Twenty.

Unconscious control can also be a disadvantage if you want to change a particular behaviour. Some automatic behaviours can turn into undesirable habits, and breaking habits usually requires conscious intervention. You may have to consciously intervene each time the trigger occurs in order to break the habit, until the unconscious mind understands that the behaviour has been replaced. You have to practise undoing the behaviour in the same way you had to practise doing it originally. This means you must be alert to the trigger all the time, which requires discipline, and can be a challenge given the limited capacity of the conscious mind.

Just recognising the trigger can be problematic. It could be any sensory input, internal or external, or an emotion, or a combination of those. The sensory input may be filtered out by your unconscious mind and not even enter conscious awareness.

The emotion could have a multitude of causes. Some behaviours have multiple triggers. By the time you realise that you are engaging in the habit, it may be too late to identify the trigger. It is not surprising that breaking some habits poses such a challenge!

If your unconscious mind believes the habit is a form of protection, it will be reluctant to release it. Most of the time this is beneficial, like checking for traffic before crossing the road. It means you can live safely without having to overload your conscious mind with details. However, it may keep repeating old habits that are no longer appropriate because it believes it is performing its primary function, which is to protect you. The unconscious mind is not logical and may not recognise when habits become outdated. In this case it is useful to understand how to communicate with your unconscious mind to break the habit.

The unconscious mind developed before the complicated language we now use. It processes information in symbolic form and, in order to communicate with it, you must learn the symbols it uses. As the unconscious mind exerts a great deal of control and is incredibly powerful, it can be very beneficial to exchange messages with it. The unconscious mind is also the source of creativity, so if you are seeking new ideas or the solution to a problem, communicating with your unconscious mind may provide you with inspiration.

While you sleep, the unconscious mind creates dreams which often contain messages. I believe this subject is so significant and potentially powerful, I have dedicated a chapter to it (see Chapter Nineteen).

There are several ways the unconscious mind may communicate with you while you are awake. Some people say they just get a feeling that something is right, or they feel uncomfortable and sense something is wrong. They may shiver or feel tingly or tight in a certain part of their body. They may call this a hunch, or intuition, or a gut feeling. Usually it is the unconscious mind offering a message. If you sometimes get such feelings, give them your full attention. Allow yourself to fully experience the feeling and intensify it if it is not uncomfortable for you. This may help you interpret the message. If not, you may find the symbolism and metaphors described in Chapter Nineteen useful to help decipher the message.

Another method of communication is through images. Do you ever think you see something unusual or out of context for a second before realising it is just a trick of the light? Or do you regularly make similar images out of the shape of clouds or the way shadows fall? Do you frequently doodle the same pictures? These could be messages from your unconscious mind. Examine if the images have any relevance to circumstances in your life or an important decision you have to make.

A common way the unconscious mind signals us is through language. Sometimes you may be talking and the wrong word slips out of your mouth. This is often called a 'Freudian slip'. It may change or reverse the meaning of what you are saying and could be a message that what you are saying is in conflict with your thoughts. For example, you might be planning to say "I'm interested in joining your scheme"; even though you are cautious because you think there may be some unethical practices. What you actually say is "I'm interested in joining your scam."

In the above example, you are aware of your feelings towards the scheme, but sometimes a Freudian slip may indicate a conflict between your conscious and unconscious minds that you are unaware of. Someone may consciously believe they are committed to eating healthily and reducing their food intake, but when telling a friend they say, "I am committed to eating heartily." Perhaps their unconscious mind believes that they must eat heartily to stay healthy. This might explain why they still find they are eating large meals despite their conscious commitment. If there is a conflict between your conscious and unconscious minds, your unconscious mind has so much control that it will almost always win. You need to resolve any conflicts before you can achieve your conscious desires.

Sometimes a conflict can be indicated with gestures. A person may insist that they are happy to meet your colleague, while shaking their head. They are probably oblivious to the head movement because it comes from the unconscious mind. Consciously they want to appear sociable, but there may be some unconscious anxiety about meeting new people. Practise noticing your body language while you are talking. This is not always easy, and you may have to enlist the help of a friend to point out any incongruities between your words and actions.

Some gestures or habits are metaphors for unconscious thoughts. For example, biting your lip may be an indication that you should not say what you are thinking or that you are having to force yourself not to speak your opinion. Biting your nails may be a way of curbing your aggression, as nails are virtual claws that an animal may use as a weapon. Losing your voice may suggest you feel you are not being heard.

The English language has a large vocabulary and often there are many words you could have used to convey the same meaning. The words you actually choose can reveal the workings of your unconscious mind. Someone who often says "I can't afford to miss this opportunity", or "I can't afford another mistake" may have an unconscious concern about finances. Notice the words or phrases you use habitually and explore if they could be giving you a message.

Most people use some or all of the above ways of communication. Once you have recognised the ones you use most often, you can begin to understand how your unconscious mind attempts to communicate with you. With practice and experimentation, you can learn to interpret the messages more quickly and accurately. Once your unconscious mind realises that you are alert to these messages it will probably offer more of them. This can be very enlightening and provide you with a wealth of useful information about yourself. When I recognise a message, I say out loud "Thank you unconscious mind", to confirm I have received it.

Even more empowering is being able to communicate your conscious thoughts to your unconscious mind. The unconscious mind follows orders from your conscious mind as long as they don't conflict with an unconscious protection mechanism.

In the example above where someone said they were committed to eating heartily, perhaps in the past they had been seriously ill and become very weak. Their health and even their life may have depended on them eating heartily to regain their strength. If it took many months to recover to full health, the unconscious mind may have made the behaviour of eating well a habit as a survival mechanism. It may believe that releasing the habit will result in ill-health or even death, so may require a little persuading. Persuasion is easier if you know how to communicate with your unconscious mind.

If you consciously decide to stand up, your unconscious mind will follow this order and co-ordinate the muscle movements to make it happen. This happens through your thoughts; you just think what you want to do and the action follows. You may just feel thirsty, and that feeling instructs your unconscious mind to pour a glass of water. So your thoughts and feelings are being accepted by your unconscious mind all the time. This is a key point, and means that your thoughts and feelings determine your reactions and behaviours.

Whatever you concentrate on or habitually think is likely to become a reality for you. What do you feel about yourself? Do you feel like a successful, or lucky, or confident, or happy person? If you feel these things, your unconscious mind will accept the message and create success, luck, confidence or happiness (or all of them) in your life. If you think you are a failure, unlucky, nervous, clumsy or miserable, the message will pass into your unconscious mind and it will follow your orders and strive to create these things in your life. The more positive thoughts and feelings you have, the more positive your life will become.

Your gestures are also interpreted. If you walk around with a smile on your face or laughing, you can expect your unconscious mind to create happiness for you. Even if you feel sad, it is very difficult to stay sad while laughing out loud – try it. In fact, forcing yourself to laugh is an excellent way to change your mood if you are feeling miserable. If you walk around with your shoulders back and head held high, you are sending a message of confidence. Drop your shoulders and hang your head, and your unconscious mind will respond by making you feel nervous or depressed.

How do you see yourself? What do you see when you look in the mirror? Do you notice your positive attributes or do you ignore them all and focus on the few negative attributes? Practise recognising the positive aspects of yourself. The mental image you have of yourself may not be accurate, but your unconscious mind will assume it is an instruction and guide you towards behaviours that are likely to make the image a reality. If you have a clear mental picture of your body being slim and healthy, your skin smooth, your hair shiny and in good condition, you can expect this to be realised. If you regard yourself as a fat, spotty, unhealthy person with lifeless hair, you will most likely find yourself choosing an unhealthy lifestyle that may cause these attributes to become a reality.

What do you notice in the world, the positive scenes or the negative ones? Whatever you give your attention to will form your inner impressions. Some things can appear either good or bad, depending on your perspective. If your impression of the world is generally positive, you will probably see good things; if negative, bad things will attract your attention. Don't only watch depressing news reports, but search for positive stories and see the good in the world. Focus on and acknowledge positive aspects of your environment.

Even in situations that you perceive as negative, there are always positive aspects, always things to be grateful for. It is a good habit to regularly review the things you have and to express your gratitude for them. You might include your health, job, accommodation, family, friends, possessions, musical ability, creativity, positive memories and experiences. I recommend you make a list of everything you are grateful for and add to it as you think of more things.

I have heard some people say that when they are worried about something, they imagine the worst that can possibly happen so that they know how bad it could be, and if it is better it will be a pleasant surprise. Don't do this! If you imagine the worst, your unconscious mind will strive to create it. Concentrate on the best outcome and cultivate a positive attitude in all situations.

Think about the words or phrases you regularly use, because these are all interpreted by your unconscious mind as instructions. The more times you use a particular phrase, the more powerful it becomes. If you often say, "I'm happy to do that", the instruction and likely outcome is happiness. If you keep saying how fed up you are with everything, don't be surprised if you find yourself overeating. I often hear people saying "I'm afraid I can't do that" or "I'm afraid not." They are encouraging fear, which is probably the most debilitating emotion. Even if you don't mean the phrase literally, it will be interpreted literally because the unconscious mind knows no difference. This is the basis for affirmations.

Affirmations are phrases that you repeat to yourself often in order to persuade your unconscious mind that something is true. For example, if you are nervous about giving presentations, you could affirm to yourself "I am a confident presenter." Think it to yourself often and say it out loud whenever you can do so without embarrassment. The more frequently you affirm something, the sooner it becomes a reality for you. While you think or say your affirmation, assume a confident posture and imagine how you will feel when you are confident, to make it more effective. Singing your affirmation or saying it rhythmically appeals to the creative nature of your unconscious mind and encourages it to be accepted more easily.

The unconscious mind does not process the word 'not'. If I tell you the car is not blue, what do you think? You probably think about a blue car. You don't know what colour it is; it could be red, green, yellow, black, silver or any other colour - all you know is that it isn't blue. Blue is what your mind has registered. Similarly, if you think or say "I am not angry", your unconscious mind registers anger, which is exactly what you wanted to avoid. Phrase all your affirmations positively, perhaps saying "I am calm" instead.

The affirmation must always be personal, so will normally begin with 'I' or 'My'. Keep the phrase short and clear and in the present tense. If you say "I will be happy", your unconscious mind might think you mean you want happiness in the future, not now. As tomorrow never comes, you may be waiting a long time to be happy. Say instead "I am happy" or "My life is filled with happiness."

Imagining positive circumstances can be very powerful,

especially if you can make mental pictures easily. This is often called visualisation and has become quite popular as a self-help technique. It is also used by sports psychologists to foster a positive or winning attitude. Create a picture of how you want to appear, or the outcome of a particular situation. In the presenter example, you may see yourself giving a presentation, looking confident and being appreciated by your audience. Make the picture large, colourful and bright in your mind, animate it and add lots of detail.

If you are finding an unwanted habit difficult to break, you can use the methods described to communicate your desires to your unconscious mind. For example, if you want to break a nail biting habit, you could affirm: "I have strong, attractive nails", and imagine your hands and nails the way you want them to look and feel. It can sometimes be useful to analyse why you indulged in the habit in the first place, and there is more information in later chapters to help you understand your motivations for the things you do. Some habits were formed as a result of fear or nervousness, so it may also be helpful to affirm: "I am safe", or "I am confident", or other appropriate phrase.

So to communicate your desires to your unconscious mind, you can use thoughts, words, visualisation, gestures and posture. If you can combine some or all of these to portray your message, you increase your chances of success. This method works because your unconscious mind cannot distinguish between what is real (the external world) and what you have fabricated in your mind. And as we will see in the next chapter, there may not actually be any distinction.

Your unconscious mind is most open to suggestion immediately upon waking and just before going to sleep. You can reach a similar state using deep relaxation techniques, meditation and self-hypnosis, which are discussed in Chapter Seventeen. These are the best times for directed communication, but frequent repetition is also important, so use other times throughout the day. Even if you have no specific instructions, your first and last thoughts of the day are very influential, so make sure they are positive. I believe the phrase "He got out of bed the wrong side this morning", which is usually used to explain why someone is grumpy, is an indication that we realise our first thoughts and actions when we wake up can affect our attitude for the whole day.

If you have negative thoughts on your mind when you go to bed, use some of the techniques described above to change them. If the thoughts are persistent, imagine bundling them all up and throwing them out of the window or burying them in a field. Some people find writing down their feelings or composing a letter to the person who triggered the unwanted thoughts is helpful. Don't send the letter; destroy it in some way when you have said all you want to. Other people find shouting "Be gone" releases negative thoughts.

The inability of the unconscious mind to distinguish between what is 'real' and what is not can have other implications. Anyone who frequently watches violent films may eventually come to believe that the world is a violent place, or worse, that violence is acceptable, even heroic. Regular viewers of soap operas may think that the behaviour of the actors is normal and copy it. They cannot appreciate that it is dramatised for entertainment. I do wonder how many immoral acts are inspired by films or television. One of the reasons advertising works is that your unconscious mind takes in what it sees and hears, and the advertiser's message is reinforced each time the advert is repeated.

Computer games may also have undesirable ramifications. Some games encourage fighting an opponent and reward the player for injuring or killing them. If their character is shot, the bullets do not hurt. If their character gets killed, they are presented with another life. When the player is young with an immature and impressionable mind, who knows what thoughts become lodged in their unconscious mind?

In some games the player is driving a car. Some of the simulations are quite realistic, yet the driver does not have to consider any of the dangers of driving. There is no threat to their life, no pain when the car crashes, either physical or financial. The objective is often to drive as quickly as possible in order to win. If the car crashes, they are given another virtual car. They may even win more points by crashing or destroying other cars.

The unconscious mind remembers everything, and I wonder how many of these experiences influence the player when they drive a real car on the public roads.

Emotions come from the unconscious mind. Sometimes you may feel a particular emotion for no apparent reason. Perhaps something happened outside your awareness, but your unconscious mind registered it and believed it was appropriate to alert you. You cannot consciously control an emotion. You can choose how you react to it, or you can suppress it. If you suppress it, it does not disappear; it either bubbles just below your awareness ready to burst out again, or is stored in your cells, as discussed in Chapter Twenty-one.

An emotion that has been suppressed or repressed is unresolved. In order to be resolved, it must enter your conscious mind. Your unconscious mind will present you with an emotion for resolution when it believes you are ready to resolve it. If you notice you are frequently experiencing anger, perhaps there is an angry incident from the past that requires resolution. It may seem like you are angry because of someone or something else, but anger is just one possible response, and you chose to respond in that way for a reason. The anger came from within you, not from the other person or the incident.

When you feel the emotion just allow yourself to experience it if at all possible. Feel it, notice where in the body it resides and any attributes it may have such as colour, texture and sound. You may find images or sounds spontaneously occurring. Don't fight or judge the experience; accept it as part of you, which of course it is. Realise that it is OK to have the emotion. If it is appropriate, allow yourself to clench your fist, tense your jaw or do whatever you feel you want to do as long as it causes no harm to yourself or others. You have to experience the emotion in order to release it. Sometimes release is associated with insight or resolution of other issues, even physical health problems.

If you can, intensify the experience and allow it to dissipate in its own time. I find this is easier when sitting or lying in a relaxed way with no distractions. I acknowledge that I am safe and just allow the feelings to occur and move around my body.

Sometimes I feel the sensation of something flowing away, out of my feet, and I interpret this as the negativity leaving me. If experiencing the emotion is too painful for you, it may help to become a detached observer. You may imagine floating above yourself or stepping to one side temporarily. Your body is experiencing the emotion, but you are detached from it. You may have to do this several times to completely release a particular emotion.

If the situation does not allow you to experience it immediately, make time to recreate the feelings as accurately as possible when you have the time. If you don't, another issue will probably cause similar emotions at a later time, so it is better to provide the opportunity for resolution when it is convenient, rather than risk an unpleasant situation in circumstances where you have less control.

If you believe you are not an emotional person, it may be that you are repressing some of your emotions. This often happens if you consider a certain emotion inappropriate or unacceptable. Rather than admit you have it, you suppress it. You may react without being fully aware of the emotion, sometimes fabricating an apparently plausible, rational explanation for your reaction. Everyone has emotions and it is in your interest to acknowledge and accept yours. You may find some of the techniques described in the following chapters helpful in this respect.

The concepts presented in this chapter form the basis for many of the techniques described in later pages. It is important you understand and accept these concepts in order to derive the maximum benefit from the following topics. Understanding the way your unconscious mind works can provide you with new ways of thinking and therefore increases the number of possibilities open to you.

Chapter 13

Your Reality

The world you perceive to be outside of yourself is actually internal, in your mind. We all have a unique model of the world, based on many factors, including our past experiences, our interests, prejudices, beliefs and the way we process information.

Four people sitting together may look out of the same window. One may see the tree outside, but has no particular interest in trees so makes no further distinction. Another, a landscape gardener, notices the way the leaves are hanging, the tinges of brown on the leaves, the unusual texture of the bark, and wonders if the tree is diseased. The third person, an ornithologist, barely registers the tree, but is fascinated by the pair of goldfinches pecking insects off one of the branches. The fourth, an agoraphobic, sees nothing but open space, and feels fearful.

So what you consciously extract from the vast amount of data presented and absorbed by your unconscious mind may be very different from what anyone else remembers about the same situation. This explains why witnesses to a crime or incident may report very different accounts of the event. Their recollection of the event is influenced by many factors, including their particular interests, their primary representational system (explained later in this chapter), the filters they put on the world, their emotional state at the time, an aspect of themselves they would rather not face, and countless other things that make us all individual. As your reality determines the way you live your life and the decisions you make, it is empowering to understand as much about your model of the world as possible.

Many of the experiences that shaped your reality occurred a long time ago, in infancy and childhood when you were immature and naiive. You may not be able to recall the incidents now, but the conclusions you drew all those years ago, however flawed or misguided, could still be influencing you now. As a young child you were very impressionable, and lacked the capacity to reason.

For example, consider a toddler who is approached by an inquisitive, small dog. The dog puts its nose into the girl's face in an attempt to find out more about her. The dog seems huge and threatening to the girl and she is terrified, but she is unable to run away from it. Those few fearful seconds before she is rescued by an adult seem like an eternity to her. In order to protect her from similar potential dangers in the future, the girl's unconscious mind may create an aversion to dogs. This may be reasonable while she is small and vulnerable, but if nothing happens to alter her perception of dogs, she may carry the aversion into adulthood. She may become unnecessarily tense in the presence of small, harmless dogs, or even have a phobia about dogs.

Not all our reactions are as straightforward as the above example. Consider a young boy's first experience of bonfire night. Perhaps he was handed a hotdog and just caught the smell of it at the same time as the first firework exploded. The loud bang startled him and his unconscious mind made the connection between the smell of the hotdog and the fear he felt, even though the two were unrelated. In later life, he may find the smell of hotdogs unpleasant and avoid them whenever possible. Remember that the unconscious mind is not logical. It makes decisions aimed at protecting you, based on the information it has available at the time.

Connections may be made in all sorts of circumstances, not necessarily for protection. I remember my niece as a baby holding a key ring that played different sounds. She didn't know how to press the buttons to make the noises, but she clung onto it as she lay on her back on the floor. As she swung her arms around, her elbow hit the floor, causing her thumb to touch one of the buttons, producing an exciting sound. She liked this so much that she banged her elbow on the floor again. Making the connection that this was the way to produce the sounds that she enjoyed, she proceeded to bang her elbow repeatedly. I think this must have hurt, but presumably the pleasure of the noise was worth it. That particular connection was later modified of course, but it serves to illustrate the point.

I believe the jealously and sometimes hatred children feel towards their siblings is based on the protection and survival mechanism. The immature mind may think that if someone else can take the attention of their parent or guardian away from them, that may place them in danger. This is true to an extent, but to the vulnerable child, it may seem life-threatening enough for them to want to destroy the competition. This might explain why there are often fights between siblings. Some children wish for some catastrophe to befall their brother or sister. If their sibling then becomes ill or has an accident, they may believe their negative thoughts were the cause. They may then experience guilt and conclude they are an evil person. Again, it is not logical, but it is not uncommon for children to make such connections and believe unrelated incidents are their fault.

Thankfully, most of us have enough experiences as we go through childhood to allow us to live in relative harmony with our siblings. However, I do know of people who have carried their jealousy into their adulthood, allowing it to affect their relationship with their siblings throughout their life. In a loving and nurturing family, any thoughts the child has of being evil can be dispelled, but I do wonder how many of our negative or unsupportive beliefs about ourselves are rooted in our long forgotten and spurious early interpretations.

The first step to understanding more about your reality is awareness. Just notice the way you feel and react in certain situations, and start to detect any patterns. This way you can bring unconscious reactions into your conscious mind and have the opportunity to intercept and change them. You have a choice about how to react in any situation. There are many possible reactions, but you may be locked into one response out of habit and conditioning.

Let's consider a situation at work where your boss asks you if you have finished the piece of work he assigned to you. You have not completed it yet. Informative and professional replies might include "No, I'm hoping it will be ready by the end of next week"; "No, I am finding it more complex than I originally thought and I would like to request some assistance"; "No, some other work took priority so we need to rework the schedule";

"No, I'd like to discuss my other responsibilities and prioritise my work."

In the past, you may have taken longer than anticipated on a particular project and been disciplined for it. Or you may believe that your promotion depends on impressing your boss. Or you may have received a lot of criticism in your formative years, which now clouds all your interactions. Or there could be other aspects of your reality that may cause you to feel defensive about the question. This might prompt you to react inappropriately based on emotion. I have heard responses similar to "Your schedule was wildly optimistic; you should go on a project planning course"; "I had finished it but my disk crashed and now I've lost the lot"; "How do you expect me to finish it when you keep on giving me all this other work?"; "Sorry, I'm obviously not up to the job. You had better assign it to someone more competent."

Other people may say very little except to pretend they have almost finished, then sit quietly fuming about the unfairness of it all. Their reality has caused them to make assumptions about the purpose behind the question. Just as your reality is unique to you and unknown to anyone else, your boss's reality is a mystery to you. However well you know someone, you can never fully understand their internal world. You do not know the reason for the question, so it is best not to jump to conclusions. Learn to delay your initial reaction to give yourself a chance to analyse your response. This need only take a few seconds. Just remember that what you perceived as an accusation, criticism, attack or insult, only becomes so if you allow it to.

Let's examine perceived criticism by way of example. If you were criticised (told off) as a child by your mother, your immature mind may have interpreted this as lack of love, especially if it was accompanied by annoyance, as it often is. You may have thought that if she didn't love you, she may abandon you and this would threaten your survival.

In this scenario, criticism could be a very bad thing. It may be that you feared criticism so much because of the potential threat, you searched for it in every interaction – and if you searched thoroughly enough, you could probably convince yourself it was there. Some people can turn around even the most innocent of remarks and infer criticism.

I remember discreetly pointing out to a work colleague as he arrived at the office that he had his T-shirt on inside-out. I thought this was a helpful remark that would allow him to change it and avoid embarrassment. Instead of being grateful, he apparently took it as a criticism and retorted angrily that he liked it that way round so that the seams did not chaff his skin. However, I noticed a little later on that he had reverted to wearing it the more conventional way.

If you have gone through life finding criticism where there was none, you may discover you have a pretty low opinion of yourself. No matter how hard you try, it seems that someone always criticises you. You may wonder why you bother and become depressed. Or you may set yourself increasingly high standards to try and prove yourself, working harder and harder, but as you can probably find criticism in praise and recognition, it is an impossible goal. The solution is to change your model of the world. Instead of finding criticism, search for something positive. It is just as easy to find the positive as the negative if you allow yourself to; it's just a different interpretation.

It can be interesting to identify the situations that could have caused you to develop your perceptions about yourself, but it isn't necessary. It is more important to recognise your tendencies and use your adult reasoning ability to change them. As soon as you feel a negative emotion surfacing, stop and search for as many positive things as you can. Detach yourself from the emotion and consider the situation logically and rationally. Think of other possible interpretations. This may take practice and persistence.

Writing down your thoughts can be helpful and may help to release negativity. If you often feel insulted, consider why a particular remark had this effect on you. Was it really intended as an insult, or was it a joke or an innocent observation? Do you have low self-esteem and assume that every comment is derogatory? Assume it was just a casual remark and notice how this changes your reaction. If you can, ask for clarification of what was meant; you may be surprised by the reply.

In some circumstances, you may decide that the comment or action really was intended as a criticism or attack of some kind. If it is justified, accept it and do what you can to rectify the situation. It's not the end of the world if someone has a different opinion from you – it just confirms that we are all unique and have different personal realities. Don't dwell on your mistake or inadequacy. Be grateful for the feedback and use it as an opportunity to learn about yourself and to react more appropriately in future. We all make mistakes; it's part of life and learning.

If the attack is not justified, it is likely that the person giving it feels threatened by you for some reason. Perhaps they perceive you as more successful, attractive, wealthy, respected or admired. They may be repeating patterns of behaviour from the past that are no longer appropriate and feel the need to destroy the opposition as in sibling rivalry. Realise that they must be very fearful to feel the need to attack you or put you down. Feel compassion towards them and accept they have their own problems and misconceptions. Don't allow their problems to become your problems by retaliating, although if there are other people involved, you may want to clarify the situation with them in a calm and mature way.

A trusted friend may be able to help you identify patterns in your behaviour. If you do ask for their assistance, you must be willing to consider their feedback. It may feel as though they are criticising you, but do not allow yourself to react in a defensive or counter-attacking way. They are trying to help you and if you immediately disregard their observations, they will probably be reluctant to help for long.

The more you can detach yourself from the event under scrutiny and act as an observer of yourself, the more insight you are likely to receive. The experiences of your life that determine the way you react are unique to you, so somebody else may not understand your reactions. Just accept that and realise that a friend can only help up to a point, and some of the analysis is your responsibility.

I hope you can now understand that the world you believe

to be external is only in your mind. You may accept that the way we interpret the world is different for all of us, but some may argue that there are events going on in the external world, so reality can't all be in your mind. This may or may not be true, but what about the things happening that you do not know about – do they exist? They don't for you. And the things you do know about are so distorted because of what your unconscious mind has chosen to ignore, how do you know what the definitive reality is?

All the things you believe to be external are in fact the memories that come from your mind. If you describe an event, you are describing your memory of it. Memories can be altered and even invented. Have you ever been told a story about your childhood that you cannot remember? Then it is recounted to you so many times you think you start to recall it? Is this really your recollection, or are you just creating the memory from what you have been told? You can create vivid and detailed memories from stories you hear and read, so much so that they can appear real to you. How do you know that your recreation of the external world bears any resemblance to the true reality?

Some people believe that there is no external world and we create our entire life in our mind. All the external events, the people with whom we interact, are all just fabrications of our mind. This is not so far-fetched as it may sound. In dreams you create all the people and resources you need, and during the dream it all seems real to you. It is not until you wake up that you realise it was all a fantasy. It is conceivable that we are all currently in a dream, but we don't realise it while we are immersed in it.

Whatever you choose to believe, it is very empowering to recognise that your reality consists entirely of memories, and that you are capable of changing, discarding or updating your memories. Just think what it would do for your self-confidence if you could change the memories of all those times you felt humiliated. We will be exploring this in Chapter Twenty.

Your personal beliefs can be so ingrained that you may not even recognise you have them. They may be adopted from your culture or family, or they may have formed through your experiences. Beliefs are not always realistic, and yours could be holding you back or preventing you from achieving your desires. The first step to changing a belief is to identify it.

For example, do you believe you will suffer illness in old age, are too young for promotion, are too short to make the basketball team or have a poor memory? None of these things is necessarily true, but if they are part of your unconscious belief system, you may act as if they *are* true and miss out on many opportunities. If you feel restricted in a certain aspect of your life, explore the belief that could be preventing you from achieving what you want. When you have identified it, you can use the techniques described elsewhere in this book to change it for the better.

Sometimes beliefs are formed and perpetuated through labels that others have given us. Children who are told they are gifted often perform better even if they really showed no exceptional talents. People who are labelled as having a certain condition or syndrome may follow the normal course of it because they are given expectations of how it will progress. They believe this will happen to them, so their unconscious mind creates the reality in line with their beliefs.

If you often describe yourself using a label, you are more likely to conform to the way that people who are similarly labelled behave. For example, if you label yourself as a poor communicator, this becomes part of you and you can use it as an excuse when there is a misunderstanding. If you accept you can learn good communication techniques, you change the belief and take back control of your communication.

Changing your beliefs can be extremely powerful and can cause many changes to your personal reality. Don't just accept information that concerns you to be true, especially if it adversely affects your health or happiness. Believe that you control your reality and that your mind has the power to achieve many things.

The science of Neuro-Linguistic Programming (NLP) provides some insight into the ways in which we construct our internal world. It proposes that we all have a preferred way of processing information, which is usually either visual, auditory, kinaesthetic or digital. Gustatory (taste) and olfactory (smell) are less common. We may all use combinations of these to represent our experiences, but we usually tend towards one, called the primary representational system.

Someone whose primary representational system is visual prefers to use images. Thoughts and memories are often dominated by pictures and scenes. The word 'bird' usually causes an image of a bird to be generated. For auditory people, sounds are often the most important feature of an experience. The word 'bird' may bring forth the sound of birdsong. For those who are primarily kinaesthetic, feelings dominate their experiences. The word 'bird' may trigger the feel of feathers. The digital representation is quite uncommon and seems to be emerging from the modern world of computers and technology. It is logical, precise and often sequential. The word 'bird' may generate thoughts of a precise number of birds, perhaps lined up in an orderly fashion.

It is useful to identify your primary representational system. If you don't already know what it is, think back to your last holiday. What is the first thing that comes into your mind? For example, it might be the beautiful views or the colour of the sea (visual), the sounds of the waves lapping on the beach or the music that played in the pub (auditory), the heat of the sun on your skin or the comfort of your accommodation (kinaesthetic), or the date and time of arrival or the room number (digital).

Alternatively, think about knocking on a door. Do you see your hand on the knocker, hear the knock, feel the texture of the knocker, or count the number of knocks? Do this exercise with a number of memories until you are quite confident that you know your preferred system.

It is also useful to recognise if there is one or more systems that you use minimally. When you have the holiday thought or a similar one in your mind, add another sense to the memory until you have at least visual, auditory and kinaesthetic elements. If there is one that came less easily to you, or that you would not have included without prompting, you may want to develop this to enhance your experiences and bring more variety and richness into your life.

You can start to do this by just noticing the sensory input that is lacking. With practice you can learn to notice things that you were previously not consciously aware of. It may also help you to relate to people who process information using a different representational system from you, as explored in Chapter Sixteen.

NLP also includes theories about our habitual patterns of behaviour, termed metaprogrammes. For example, some people plan their life in the pursuit of what they want, whereas other people plan their life avoiding the things they don't want. Some people may follow the health advice in part one because they want to enjoy a long healthy life, others may follow it to avoid the pain and disruption of illness. The former is driven by desire and is preferable; the latter is driven by fear. Other metaprogrammes are discussed in Chapter Sixteen.

I encourage you to learn more about NLP and the patterns that relate to you, as it will help you to understand how you construct your reality. The more you can expand your reality, the more options you give yourself. Wider choice means more freedom and ultimately greater enjoyment of life.

Chapter 14

Emotions and Motivation

As emotions play such an important part in creating your reality, a degree of insight into your emotions can be beneficial. Recognising how they influence your reactions and perceptions can help you become more self-aware. This offers you greater flexibility when making choices, the choices that shape the quality of your life.

Some people may say that it is having emotions that makes us human, that we have risen above animals who act purely on instinct. However, close analysis of most emotions will reveal that they derive from basic instincts. Perhaps the most obvious basic instinct is that of survival. When faced with the possibility of death, people are willing to endure incredible pain, disruption, anguish or a poor quality of life just to survive. They are often willing to take huge gambles in a desperate attempt to cling to life, however tortuous that life may be.

The instinct to procreate is strong in the majority of people. It is easy to pretend the desire for children is romantic, or is to create a spiritual connection, special bond or sense of completion, but the truth is that it is instinctual to propagate our genes and perpetuate the species. This is demonstrated in the desperation of couples unable to conceive. Many are willing to undergo radical exploration and invasive techniques that remove all intimacy between the parents, and some would even consider cloning as an option in order to have offspring.

Sexual urges can be intense even in those who decide not to have children. Their sexual desires continue despite their conscious decision not to procreate. Of course, sexual contact can be intimate, loving, and physically and emotionally fulfilling, but it doesn't change the fact that the desires are basic instincts. The hormones produced by our bodies create odours which, although we are often unaware of them, can be detected by the unconscious mind. These odours constantly transmit our state of fertility and may influence the sexual urges of those around us. We are similarly sexually motivated by the olfactory signals we unconsciously detect in others. So apparently loving gestures are actually more likely to be driven by instincts.

The desire to create a comfortable home for yourself and your family is really just an advanced form of nest-building. Most people make their home secure with locks and alarms, and fence off their land to mark it as their territory. Anyone trespassing will be attacked verbally, or even physically, in a similar way that most birds and animals defend their territory.

It is important to understand the part that instincts play in your life to help you recognise the motivation behind your choices, as discussed later in this chapter. Instincts can also be considered as the pursuit of basic needs. You need light, air, water, food, sex and security, and if these needs are not met you will not be able to progress to higher levels of awareness. For example, if you do not feel secure, your unconscious mind will constantly seek to address this, which may interfere with your conscious desires.

Emotions should be considered as neither positive nor negative – they just are. The way you feel in a certain situation is simply feedback. For example, you may categorise fear as negative, but if it causes you to take evasive action that saves your life, surely that is very positive. In potentially dangerous situations, fear helps to protect you.

Emotions require both polarities in order to exist. To be able to feel happiness, you must have experienced sadness to give it some context. Although it would seem ideal to only experience love, joy, serenity, comfort and safety, these emotions would have no meaning without hate, sadness, anger, pain and fear to relate them to. So the goal is not to try and eliminate unpleasant emotions, but to embrace all emotions, recognise them as feedback and learn from them.

As emotions come from the unconscious mind, you cannot consciously control them. The purpose of an emotion may be to satisfy a basic need or instinct, to attempt to protect you, or to give you an opportunity to address unresolved issues. Accept all your emotions with gratitude.

The first few years of your life play a crucial role in your emotional development. The experiences you have as a young, impressionable child can have repercussions throughout your life, as a large portion of your reality is formed in your early years. A secure, loving family environment, where most of your physical and emotional needs are met, provides the most favourable conditions for healthy emotional development. However, most of us carry a significant amount of 'emotional baggage' into adulthood.

In adult life, certain situations can trigger particular emotions. I believe that many of the emotions we feel as adults are not caused by the situation that triggered them, but by the memory of similar situations when we were young. The current situation just stimulates old emotions.

Consider road rage. Why do people get so angry just because another car pushes in front of them in a queue? In terms of extended journey time, it probably makes a difference of a few seconds to be an extra car behind. The rage is unnecessary and unhelpful, and may cause you to drive more recklessly, compromising your safety. It is more likely to be the principle of the situation that triggers the emotion. The incident may be stimulating childhood emotions of not getting your own way, being cheated out of something, having something taken away from you or being beaten in competition.

You can probably rationalise your rage by saying the other driver wasn't following the rules of the road, or that they endangered you and other road users by driving inconsiderately. It is much easier to present a plausible explanation for your emotions over the incident than to admit the true source was having your favourite toy confiscated. Of course, you may not realise the source of the emotion because it is unconscious.

You may find that lots of different situations cause you irritation. This is usually an indication that the source of the irritation is an old emotion being stimulated. If you can identify and resolve it, you are more likely to stay calm in similar situations in the future. Techniques to help you with this are discussed elsewhere in this book. If you can't identify the emotion, at least own it and recognise it is within you and not the direct result of the circumstances.

Often it is the anticipation of what will happen that causes the emotion. If you imagine that someone will be rude to you, you may become upset before any words have even been exchanged. You may convince yourself that the other person is looking at you disparagingly, or assume they have been talking about you in a derogatory way. Once you are primed to expect the rudeness, you can interpret almost any innocent remark as rude. The more evidence you accumulate to prove your theory, however illogical or unrealistic it may be, the more you anticipate rudeness in the future. The source of this attitude may have been one incident years ago that had a strong influence on you, but instead of resolving it, you allow it to continue to affect you.

We already know that you are the only person who can affect your feelings and emotions. You react the way you do because of your personal reality. If you blame someone else for your anger, disappointment, guilt or fear, you perpetuate the cycle, ensuring other situations will stimulate the same emotions over and over again.

One of the most powerful emotions is fear. The advancements of the human race mean that we have created a relatively safe environment for ourselves with few external threats to our survival as a species. However, we still feel fear and allow it to influence many of our decisions. For example, fear of the unknown often prevents people from trying new experiences, and fear of being alone may cause some to stay in unsatisfactory relationships.

I notice how fear of failure motivates people in business and corporate environments. The desire to achieve, to become successful, to receive recognition or to prove themselves is so strong, that it causes some people to work excessively hard. They neglect all other aspects of their life, including their health and their family in order to succeed. They may claim they are creating financial security for their family or that they have no control over their workload. But we always have a choice, and choosing to work oneself into an early grave is a sure sign that the true motivation has not been recognised.

One reason for such an intense desire to succeed could be

that the individual was not praised as a child. Their achievements may not have been recognised, or were perhaps overshadowed by other events. They may have been told they would 'never come to anything' and feel they have to prove this to be wrong. They may have been the youngest in the family and always felt they were one step behind, never being able to shine above their siblings.

Another trait often evident in corporate environments is power building. Some people feel they can create personal power by climbing the corporate ladder, holding positions of influence or decision making, or being in charge of a large workforce or budget. The motivation of these people is not what is best for the company or organisation, but what will bring them greatest power. Comparisons can be drawn between this type of behaviour and the fights that occur in the animal kingdom to become dominant within the herd.

Not all people in positions of influence are motivated by personal power. However, taking on unnecessary staff, specifying unrealistically high budgets or taking dubious decisions could all be indications that there is a conflict between personal and company goals. In most cases, these motivators will be unconscious, and the person will go to great lengths to justify the decisions in a logical way.

Often the underlying reason for such behaviour is the desire to be loved and accepted. These individuals feel that if they gain success or recognition they will be loved. The influence of parental values, especially those of your mother, should never be underestimated. It is not uncommon for people to take radical or life-changing decisions based on their parents' wishes. They may pursue careers or choose partners that their parents approve of. This need for parental approval can last a lifetime, sometimes unconsciously.

Do you ever allow your life to be influenced by your parents, childhood caregivers or other special person? Have you ever not done something you wanted to do because you thought they may disapprove? Or perhaps you did it anyway, but kept it a secret from them. If the answer is yes to any of the above, (and it is in your interest to be honest with yourself), you are giving away some of your freedom and personal power.

Live your life by your own values and morals. Other people may have different values, which you should respect, but that is no reason to change yours. Accept that we are all unique and have different opinions. Some people follow their beliefs and then feel guilty because they think others may disapprove. Guilt is a self-inflicted torture. If you feel guilty about something, take any action you can to rectify the situation, learn from the episode and then move on. Holding on to guilty feelings doesn't help anyone, and it may cause you unnecessary stress that could compromise your health.

Some people think that they can gain love and acceptance through their physical appearance. Females, especially, often seek approval through external beauty. They spend enormous amounts of time and money creating an image of beauty through cosmetics, personal care products, clothing, surgery, exercise regimes and restrictive diets.

True beauty comes through loving yourself. If you love and accept yourself and your body, you will automatically be drawn to a lifestyle that supports your physical and emotional health. You will be more relaxed and comfortable with yourself, and this will be reflected in your appearance. If you are always anxious about the way you look, the stress will take its toll on your posture, your skin, your eyes, and your internal functions, affecting your overall health and the way you present yourself to the world.

The problem with using external factors as motivators is that they don't address the root cause of the issue. Personal power, confidence, and self-love have to come from within. Deep, lasting fulfilment rarely comes from external sources. That is why the CEO never feels successful and keeps driving harder to achieve more, the attractive female keeps trying new cosmetics in an attempt to create the perfect appearance, the athlete trains more intensively despite being a winner and the scholar studies for more and more qualifications.

Sometimes emotions can become overwhelming, resulting in irrational behaviour, depression or mental disorders. Often the root cause of the emotion is a deep unconscious fear, possibly a perceived threat to survival. It may be triggered by an apparently trivial event but can result in feelings of devastation, desperation and hopelessness. Accept that your unconscious mind is doing what it believes is necessary to protect you, however illogical it may seem.

If you find yourself in a state of depression, use some of the techniques described elsewhere in this book to communicate with your unconscious mind for insight into the underlying problem. If you are not emotionally stable enough to concentrate on these, start by engaging in some physical activity, even if you don't feel like it. An emotional blockage usually has an associated energy blockage in the body, and exercise and movement can help this to disperse. Concentrating on something else can also create a temporary distraction and may provide the opportunity to take a different perspective on the issue.

It can be helpful to remember that emotions come and go, memories fade and situations change. However hopeless your circumstances may seem to you, there is always hope. Think back to situations in your life that seemed impossible at the time, and reflect on the fact that you made it through. Find some positive aspects of your life to appreciate. If possible, find something that makes you laugh.

I believe that there is a large element of unconscious motivation in our choice of friends and partners. We seek the qualities in others that we lack ourselves. You may have heard the phrase 'opposites attract'. So a person who feels weak or vulnerable may choose a partner who appears to be strong. Someone lacking in self-confidence may be attracted to a person with confidence. This can even extend to physical attributes – short people may choose tall partners, fat people may choose thin partners.

This selection is flawed because you can never truly know how someone else feels. A person who appears confident may not actually be confident. Physical strength does not necessarily imply emotional strength. People can change, and attributes they have at the start of a relationship may alter over time.

Even if you successfully find a partner who has the qualities you lack, it does not address your emotional issues. For example, if you are lacking in self-love, you may choose a partner who frequently demonstrates their love for you through words and loving gestures. Your desire to be loved may then be temporarily met. However, because you don't love yourself, you may doubt how they can love you and wonder if they are being honest. Or their gestures may become expectations, so if they are absent for some reason, you may assume that means they don't love you any more. If you are convinced you are unlovable, you may not recognise the gestures, or misinterpret them.

However happy you are in your current circumstances, it is well worth becoming more self-aware. In fact, when you are calm and relatively stable is a good time to evaluate your motivations. Your circumstances may change, and the more you understand about yourself, the better you will be able to adapt. For example, any feelings of insecurity may not be evident if you have a happy family life, good health, a home of your own, a secure job and source of income, but if any of those disappear it is likely that you will feel insecure again. A feeling of security and trust in life comes from within.

If your plans are not working as you expected, you may want to have an honest review of your real motivations. There may be some conflict between your conscious and unconscious minds. For example, you may claim you want to spend more time with your family, but then take a job that involves a lot of travel and trips away from home. Or you may say your goal is to become fit and healthy, yet you consistently avoid taking exercise and frequently eat junk food. You can use the techniques described in this book to communicate with your unconscious mind and gain insights into your motivations.

When your conscious and unconscious minds are in harmony you will find your life flows more easily. You will be attracted to people and situations that assist you on your life's path. This attraction is called synchronicity and can be very beneficial. It causes you to be in the right place at the right time. Chance meetings may turn out to provide you with a vital piece of information.

Synchronicity can also create situations that may seem unpleasant to you. The most likely explanation is that your unconscious mind has drawn you into the situation so you can learn from it and resolve important issues. This concept is explored in more depth later in this book.

A degree of self-love and acceptance is required to form your identity. Before they have their own identity, young people often identify with a gang, a particular fad, or fashionable possessions. Ideally, they will grow out of this and become comfortable enough with themselves to discard these external symbols. However, this does not always happen, and some people feel the need for symbols of beauty, power or status throughout their adult life.

I heard a famous entertainer explain how she dieted and dropped from a size 22 to a slim size twelve for her wedding day. But she said she felt it 'wasn't me', so she quickly put all the weight back on. It sounds to me as though she had identified with being a fat person, and being slim felt unfamiliar. She preferred her familiar, less healthy body because she had made it part of her identity.

Some people identify with a particular behaviour because someone they respect or admire indulges in it. Smokers often start their habit to be like their hero or their popular friend who happens to smoke. Recognising that they have associated smoking with their identity can help them to change their image of themselves and break the habit. Smoking is also used as a way of repressing emotions, as the physical actions can be used to occupy the mind and keep emotions at bay.

People identify with all sorts of things and make them part of their image, including flashy cars, academic qualifications, their home, taking holidays in exotic locations and expensive jewellery. There is nothing wrong with enjoying these things if you can afford them, but if you have to take a second job or take out loans to cover the cost, it is a possibility that they are a substitute for your identity.

You can probably argue that you deserve a nice holiday, you need a car, or that extra qualifications will help you to advance your career. It is easy to compose a logical explanation for your behaviours, but you will benefit more by examining your motivations more closely. You don't necessarily have to change immediately; just recognising you may have a hidden agenda is progress on your journey towards self-awareness.

If you feel you have to own certain possessions or socialise in particular circles to be accepted by others, this probably indicates that you are not accepting yourself as you are. Acceptance and respect from others starts with accepting yourself. Happiness comes from within, not from conforming to an image you think will gain approval. And spending time and money maintaining your image may mean you miss out on the things that will bring you lasting happiness and fulfilment.

Your emotions influence every decision you make and sometimes the real motivation can be unconscious. As you explore and accept your emotions, your identity becomes more stable and you understand yourself better. With understanding comes control, and more conscious control and awareness means you are freer to make the choices that will bring health and happiness into your life.

Chapter 15

Communication

We have explored how you may be able to communicate with yourself, but to live in this world you must be able to communicate with others. An inability to be understood and make your needs and wants clear can lead to frustration and dissatisfaction. I believe that good communication is fundamental to creating successful and fulfilling relationships, both professional and personal. It is usually a requirement for achievement and advancement. Poor communication can lead to wasted time and effort and could compromise your health and happiness.

When most people consider communication, they think of language. The vocabulary and grammar that humans have developed allow us to share ideas and complex concepts. We can usually understand what others are saying and make ourselves understood well enough to ensure our needs are met.

Talking and listening have become so natural for us that we can use words imprecisely and they can often still be interpreted. However, this imprecise communication can create ambiguities and lead to misunderstandings. How often has the confusion between the responses 'yeah' and 'nah' caused you frustration? 'Yes' and 'no' are much more easily distinguished. Has someone mumbling or talking quickly caused you to interpret a completely different meaning from what was intended?

As it is mainly language that has enabled humans to make such huge technological advancements, I think it is important to use it to maximum effect. Good communication skills can lead to more productive conversations, as well as enhancing relationships. I'm not suggesting you take elocution lessons, just that you make an effort to communicate clearly. There are many aspects to communication and I will explore the ones that I think will be most beneficial to you.

Written communication has the advantage of allowing you time to consider how to phrase your message and to check your words before sending. This may be the best option if you feel nervous or uncertain about speaking to the recipient. Electronic communication is widespread and is often the preferred form of communication in professional situations. Read what you have written carefully before sending it. This sounds obvious, but I am still amazed at the number of emails I receive with spelling mistakes, grammatical errors and ambiguities that make the whole communication impossible to understand.

The way you communicate to others has a very important impact on their impressions of you. You may have the most brilliant ideas, but if you cannot express yourself well enough to share them with anyone, your brilliance will not be acknowledged. If you choose inappropriate words, you risk your message being misinterpreted and upsetting the recipient. If your written communication is riddled with errors, people may decide this is a reflection of you and that you pay no attention to detail, are lazy, or take no pride in yourself or your work. Would you entrust the management of your personal affairs to a professional who can't even spell your name correctly?

You may wonder why I believe this is so important. You might notice that someone has written the word 'there' instead of 'their', or 'your' instead of 'you're', but you can still understand the intended meaning, so what's the big deal? You may be able to understand it in this instance, but this may not always be the case.

If someone has written "I am going to", they could have meant to write "I am going too", or they could have missed a word to clarify what they are going to do or where they are going. Similarly, the wrong spelling of 'too' could make the sentence "I am going to fast" ambiguous.

Or consider this example. You are doing a friend a favour and you see a note saying: "There are tickets on the table." You assume this must be a gesture of appreciation from your friend and gratefully take the tickets. But next time you meet, instead of words of thanks for your time and effort, your friend greets you with the accusation: "I knew I couldn't trust you to leave those tickets alone. I even left you a note saying they're our tickets on the table, didn't you see it?"

Unfortunately, I am discovering that many of these errors are made out of ignorance rather than haste or oversight. With the proliferation of electronic forums, chat rooms and websites with such errors, they seem to be becoming accepted. Some people may read these grammatical errors and believe they are correct, especially if their English language education was inadequate. So the inaccuracies will probably spread and our ability to communicate clearly will suffer, to the detriment of us all.

Make the effort to ensure your written notes are clear and the spelling, syntax and grammar are correct. Language is probably the most important method of communication, so it is in your interest to be as accurate as possible. If the recipient doesn't understand what you have written, it usually means your message is inappropriately composed. Imagine the repercussions if a doctor's report on a patient was inaccurate and caused the diagnosis to be misinterpreted or the wrong treatment to be administered.

Read what you have written from the perspective of the recipient before you send it. What may be obvious to you may not be clear to someone else. Do not make unfounded assumptions about their level of knowledge, their feelings or their thought processes. Avoid words or jargon that they may not understand. Consider what information they require and what they will want to know. Use plain English and short, clear sentences. This is common sense but apparently overlooked by many people who write to me!

If you are writing about something that evokes strong emotions in you, delay sending it until the emotional intensity diminishes, if possible. Perhaps you have misinterpreted something and taken offence where none was intended. Or perhaps the communication you are responding to was poorly composed and you have misunderstood it. It may be better to compose your message when you can put the matter into perspective and perhaps understand the position of the other party. An emotionally charged note may not help you get the desired result, and may make an unpleasant situation worse. It may help to enlist the help or ask the opinion of someone who is impartial.

When you are talking to someone personally, consider what you are going to say in advance if possible, rather than starting to speak without knowing how you will finish the sentence. Phrases disrupted with 'ums' and 'ers' or filler words like 'actually', 'basically', 'sort of' and 'you know', can distract the listener and may make them miss the point of what you are saying. As with written communication, tailor your words for the recipient.

It is courteous and probably more productive to state your opinion without appearing to judge or dismiss the opinion of others. Some people can accept differences of opinion quite easily, but others may take it personally. As we have already explored, some people may anticipate rejection or criticism or disrespect because of their personal reality. If you start by pointing out all the things you disagree with or don't like, they may become defensive. There are three simple rules that can help prevent emotions from undermining your communication. They can be used when talking to someone or writing to them.

Firstly, start with something positive. This could be to thank them for sharing their ideas with you, to acknowledge the time they have spent or to tell them the things you do like about their proposals. If you tend to be a critical person, this may be a challenge for you. Even if you do not object to your thoughts being rejected, acknowledge that some people do. Give them the respect they deserve by noticing the positive aspects of what they have said.

When you have given some positive feedback you can go on to what are, in your opinion, the not so positive points using the second rule, which is to suggest improvements rather than pointing out the things that are wrong with the original proposal. This is an important distinction. If you say you like the idea and you think it can be improved in a certain way, you are validating what the other person has proposed. If you suggest a 'better' way, it could be interpreted as a rejection and the person may be less inclined to accept your suggestions.

The third rule is to own your opinions but realise that not everyone will agree with them. To dismiss somebody else's ideas as rubbish is rude and disrespectful. What you really mean is that you disagree with them. Recognise that everyone has their own opinions, and there is not necessarily a right or wrong way, just a number of different options. So say "I think it would be more effective if…" in preference to "It would be more effective if…"

I also like to finish with a positive statement. So pulling these ideas together, if your partner suggests a trip to the beach, the response "That's a good idea to go out somewhere, although I would prefer to go to the forest. Thank you for that suggestion" is likely to be better received than "It's too hot for the beach." Or in a work situation "Thank you for the time you spent on this report and sending it to me so promptly. The introduction is well-written and I particularly like your ideas for the future. I think perhaps the staffing figures would have more impact if represented using a graph, and I feel the conclusion could be expanded upon. Overall, it is an excellent piece of work" is more likely to create an atmosphere of co-operation than "The staffing figures are unintelligible and the conclusion is way too short."

Speech is clearer when you hold your head up and your spine is upright. Face the person you are speaking to, as volume is lost if you look away, and the listener will not be able to read your lips to help decipher your words. Don't cover your mouth with your hand for the same reasons. Make eye contact with the listener. If you don't have the attention of the listener before you start to speak, your first few words may be lost. Echoic memory can store a few seconds of sound, so they may be able to work out what you said. This becomes more difficult if you skip the first few words, as we often do when talking colloquially. It may be better to attract the listener's attention first using their name or using introductory phrases such as "I was wondering if…" or "I was thinking…"

The same guidelines apply when you are speaking to a number of people or a large audience. In this case it is even more important to speak clearly. Slow down your delivery to take account of the different requirements of your audience, the distance between you, and the acoustic properties of the venue.

You may think that using a common language allows precise understanding between people. However, words can have different meanings for different people. The word 'table' may seem straightforward enough, but is that a dining table, coffee table, massage table, bird table, table of contents? It may not refer to a physical object but be used metaphorically, as in 'the options on the table are…'. Usually you will be able to work out the intended meaning from the context, especially for objects, and if there is any uncertainty you can probably ask for clarification.

This is not true for the words we use to label emotions and feelings. If I tell you I am happy, you don't know what that means for me. 'Happy' is a word I use to describe an internal feeling, part of my private reality. You don't know what this feels like for me. You know the feeling that you associate with being happy, but the experience is unique to you. You have a general idea that happiness is a positive emotion, not as strong as ecstasy, but better than merely being contented (probably), but you don't know how intense it might be for someone else.

So words describing feelings only give a vague idea of the actual experience. If someone says they know how you feel, what they really mean is that they have been in a similar situation and remember how they felt. It can be a supportive gesture, but realise that nobody can truly understand your feelings. We will explore this more in Chapter Sixteen.

When you are talking to someone in close proximity, the words you use may account for a very small proportion of the message you are transmitting. We communicate with our whole body through unconscious communication and body language. Sometimes you may not trust what someone is saying, or have a feeling that they are not sincere, even though their words are positive. This probably means you are detecting the communication that is not through the actual words, and it seems to conflict with what the person is saying.

Sometimes this can be quite obvious. Someone may be using words that express confidence, yet their voice is shaky, their head and body are hunched in a nervous posture, and they are breathing rapidly and fidgeting. This should signal to you there is incongruity between their thoughts and words. You may not notice the signs consciously, but the unconscious mind records everything and may want to highlight the possible contradiction to your conscious mind. You may detect this as an uncomfortable feeling or a hunch that something is not quite right.

If you notice that the person talking to you has their arms and legs crossed and is leaning away from you, this may indicate they have something to hide. Covering their mouth or avoiding eye contact may also be clues that they are uncomfortable with what they are saying. Perhaps they are not being completely open and honest with you. Their unconscious actions may be revealing their true thoughts, which conflict with their words. Does their voice tone match what they are saying? If they are describing an event as really exciting, but their voice is boring and monotonous, they are unlikely to sound convincing.

In general, if someone is relaxed and sincere about what they are saying, that will be reflected in a relaxed body and a relaxed style of speaking. If they are uneasy, their body may be tense, affecting their posture, breathing and facial expressions. Stiff shoulders, a rigid jaw, tight facial muscles and stiff lips usually indicate tension. If you are in a situation where you want to appear confident or convincing, be aware of what your body is revealing about you by noticing your posture, body language, voice tone and bodily tension. Even when talking on the telephone, voice tone, speed and pitch can reveal more than just the words being spoken.

When you want to engage in conversation with someone, in either a personal or professional capacity, building rapport will help to create an atmosphere of trust between you. The purpose of rapport is to make the other person feel that you have a common understanding, that you share their reality on this issue. This should help them relax and encourage them to talk openly and honestly, which are important aspects of successful communication.

The easiest way to start building rapport is to adopt a similar posture to the person you are conversing with. Match their general posture, especially the position of their spine. If they are leaning forward, you lean forward, if they tilt their head, you tilt your head, if they put their arms on the table, you put your arms on the table. This may sound like you are being rude or patronising, but it can be done very smoothly and naturally when an appropriate opportunity arises. This opportunity may be when the person talking becomes the listener, or when the topic changes direction or intensity. You don't have to match them exactly, just in a very general way and only when it is congruent with the situation.

Building rapport becomes easy with a little practice, and you almost certainly do it without realising when you are with someone you know and get on well with. Next time you are chatting with a friend, notice how well your posture and gestures match theirs. This is because you are relaxed with them and sharing the experience with trust.

You may also notice that you match voice tone and even accent to a certain extent when talking to others. I am not suggesting you mimic the person you are talking to, just that you notice their tonality and modify yours to be similar, within the limits of your own natural voice. If they speak slowly, slow down your speech to match. If they are talking louder or more softly than you would normally, alter the volume you use accordingly. If your voice or posture are in stark contrast to theirs, they may feel you are detached or uninterested in what they are saying. They will unconsciously detect that you are not in rapport.

The words and phrases you choose are also important. Aim to recognise their primary representational system (as described in Chapter Thirteen) early in the conversation, by paying attention to their words. Visual people may say they see what you mean, or that everything is clear. Auditory people may say that something sounds good, or rings a bell. Kinaesthetic people may say they have a good feeling about it, or you have hit the nail on the head. See the table for more examples of sensory-specific phrases.

Visual	Auditory	Kinaesthetic
I see	Rings a bell	Feels right
Crystal clear	Rings true	Holds true
Looks good	Sounds good	Feels good
Looking forward to	I hear what you say	Get a handle on
My viewpoint	Strikes a chord	Catch on
Look out	Listen up	Hold on
Eye to eye	Word for word	Hand in hand
See it through	Hear it out	Hang in there
Show up	Loud and clear	Jumps out

Examples of sensory-specific phrases

You may notice there are some people who use olfactory or gustatory phrases to describe their feelings. They may say something brings a nasty taste to their mouth, or it is a bitter pill to swallow, or that they can smell a rat. If this is the only system you can detect and you cannot think of suitable phrases to respond with, choose language with a kinaesthetic bias.

If you use words that match their system, they are more likely to understand what you are saying and feel that you have understood them. If you use only your preferred system and it is different from theirs, there may be confusion and misunderstandings.

For example, if your preferred and main system is visual, you may describe an idea or event based on the images you have of it. You may detail all the visual aspects saying what you see, the colours, the shapes and put across your viewpoint. If the listener is mainly kinaesthetic, they may not be able to create the mental image you are describing, so much of your information may be lost. They may say they can't grasp what you are saying, or can't get a handle on it, or other phrases that tend to indicate a kinaesthetic way of thinking.

Learning to converse using words and phrases from a different system does take practice, especially if you have a very strong tendency towards just one system. It is a good exercise to become aware of, and express verbally the aspects of your environment outside your preferred system. This can also help to enrich your experiences by adding variety. Listen to other people talking and start to detect patterns that could indicate their preferred system.

If they use words to describe feelings or emotions, always use the same word if you are confirming you understand what they are saying. Do not select a word that refers to what is a similar feeling for you, because this may be very different for them, as explained earlier in this chapter. If they say they are annoyed, you could respond that you understand their annoyance. If you say you understand they are frustrated, this may have a very different meaning for them. They may think you haven't been listening and don't understand what they are saying at all. Remember, the objective is to match them in their reality.

There are other ways of detecting a person's primary representational system if they do not use words that can be easily categorised into a particular system. People who are primarily visual tend to talk quickly because they can see all the details of the pictures in their mind at once. The images may be constantly changing with circumstances. Their speed of speech is an attempt to describe these images as they see them. Visual people also tend to breathe quickly from the chest.

People who are mainly kinaesthetic usually talk slowly because it takes more time to become aware of the feelings associated with the circumstances. They tend to breathe slowly from the abdomen, the location of their 'gut instincts'. The breathing of those who prefer auditory thinking is between the two, in the solar plexus area. Their speed of talking is usually a steady, even pace.

NLP also uses the concept of noticing where people move their eyes when thinking, as this can indicate if they are processing images, sounds or feelings. This can be used as a guide, but I have found the methods I have already described are more practical and reliable. If you want to learn more about eye accessing cues, as they are called, I recommend you study the fundamentals of NLP.

Attentive listening helps to build rapport. Look at the person who is talking to you, mainly at the eyes and sometimes at the mouth. Use facial expressions to acknowledge you have heard, such as smiling when they say something amusing or raising your eyebrow when they say something surprising. Nod in agreement when appropriate, or make encouraging noises if you can do so unobtrusively. Give them your full attention. Looking away, sighing or having a blank expression will inhibit them and possibly stop them talking completely.

Practise really listening to what the person is saying. If it reminds you of something, it can be tempting to stop listening and concentrate on your thoughts, but this can be disrespectful. If you consider your thought is important, just ask your unconscious mind to remind you later when it is convenient, using the techniques described in Chapter Twelve.

Some people are so enthusiastic about what they have to say, they interrupt the other person to share it. If you haven't experienced how demoralising this is, ask a friend to interrupt you a few times until you understand. To appreciate the importance of listening skills, notice how encouraging it is when someone listens to you with interest, and how dispiriting it is when they turn away, fidget or interrupt.

When you communicate effectively you can expect your life to run more smoothly and your relationships to improve. It is well worth the effort.

Chapter 16

Relationships

You can learn a great deal about yourself from your interactions with others. You have some sort of relationship with everyone you meet, so everyone is a potential teacher. Your relationships with the people you spend a lot of your time with can provide you with the most insight into yourself, and also may create the most conflict.

When you meet someone for the first time, you have to make some judgements about them to know how to react towards them. If the person is running in your direction, shouting abuse at you and holding a baseball bat above their head, you will probably perceive a threat and run for cover. Even if your judgement was not correct, your reaction is a wise precaution. The less information you have about a person, the more assumptions you have to make. Your assumptions will almost certainly be based on your previous experience, knowledge about an apparently similar person and cultural stereotypes.

If you are in a relatively safe environment, it is preferable to make few assumptions and be as open as you can. The instinct to make judgements, which to our ancestors probably made the difference between life and death, is very strong and you may not be able to prevent it. The ideas may come from your unconscious mind as a protection mechanism. Although I am in favour of being non-judgemental, I think it is impossible in some situations as we cannot consciously control our emotions.

What you can do is recognise that you have made judgements and review them consciously before acting on them. This will help you to react and interact without, or with less, prejudice. Notice the judgements you make based on gender, race, age, size, appearance, attire and accent, for example. Some judgements may be unconscious, which is why first impressions make so much of an impact. You may feel a certain way about someone but not understand why. Just acknowledge the feeling and do your best to keep an open mind.

If you feel someone is judging you unfairly, realise this may not be a conscious decision on their part. Recognise it is their model of the world that has caused them to feel the way they do, however misguided this may be. Do not react based on your emotions or feelings of injustice, as this will probably make the situation worse and reinforce their negative opinion of you. Respond calmly, using clear communication to clarify the situation and hopefully gain the respect you deserve.

Acknowledge that everyone has their own reality. The choices they have made in their life are based on their model of the world and the options they were aware of at the time. Their range of options may be different or more limited than yours, so don't judge them for making what you believe to be an unwise decision. You may find it hard to understand why someone would remain in an abusive relationship, for example, but perhaps in their reality there is no way out. Recognise that everyone is making the best choice possible for them, given the information and experiences available to them at the time.

This can be quite easy when it relates to people you meet briefly or have little interaction with. When you have drastically different ideas from your family, partner, work colleagues or someone you care for, it creates more of a challenge. Sometimes you can disagree on an issue without it affecting the relationship or the task in hand. In other situations you may have to compromise. I believe that reasonable compromise is an essential part of successful relationships, and this is discussed later in this chapter.

The way you react to certain people is a reflection of you and your reality, and you can use your reactions to learn more about yourself. Think of the things that really irritate you about other people. Perhaps it is people who play music very loudly and disturb you, or drive dangerously or very slowly, interrupt you when speaking, sniff or cough frequently, smoke near you, ignore you or are dishonest. What is it about the action that makes you feel the way you do?

If you feel angry as a result of the incident, remember that the incident didn't make you angry; you chose to be angry as a result of it. Your feelings arise from within you and nobody can cause you to feel a certain way. When you accept this and take responsibility for your feelings, you have the option to modify them. Find something positive about the incident, even if it is just to be thankful you recognise that the behaviour is inconsiderate or disrespectful.

If it is appropriate, express your feelings in some way. Otherwise just accept them and allow them to dissipate. Considering why you became angry, perhaps using the principles outlined in previous chapters, may help you to feel differently about a similar scenario in the future. It may be that you have unresolved anger from the past that your unconscious mind is presenting for you to resolve. The root of the anger may be a childhood event that is unrelated to the issue that triggered the current angry feelings.

A friend of mine had frequent conflicts with her parents even after ten years of living away from them. She felt they were always criticising her and saying how much more successful her brother and sister were. She told me she could not forgive them because they were so irresponsible and uncaring towards her. She could interpret almost anything they said as a criticism or derogatory remark, and did not recognise any of their loving gestures. She decided they hated her and found confirmation of that belief in all their interactions. She could not accept that her parents were making the best choices they could based on their reality.

As an observer, it seemed to me that her parents were understandably proud of their son and other daughter, who were exceptionally successful in business. They wanted to share their pride with my friend. She had feelings of inadequacy, despite being successful in her own field. Instead of being pleased about her siblings' achievements, she saw it as highlighting her inadequacy and responded to any remarks with anger and rudeness. This filled her parents with confusion and sadness.

My friend was so involved in the situation she could not detach herself from it and recognise that she was contributing to the ongoing unpleasantness by her reactions and counter-attacks. Her interpretation of every situation was dominated by her negative opinion of herself. Many of the conflicts were of her own creation.

Parenting may be the most important task anyone can undertake, yet we receive no formal training. Parents have to make the decisions they believe to be best at the time, despite their limited experience. They have personal issues to deal with, issues relating to their partnership and other family issues. The physical demands of parenting such as disturbed sleep, change in routine and sudden additional responsibilities can be a shock to the system. Emotional and financial demands and having to give up time that was once their own to the child add to the disruption. Hormonal changes for the mother can further increase the challenge.

It can be tempting to criticise your parents for the way they reacted in certain circumstances, advice they gave, or for your general upbringing. This does not serve any purpose except to prolong the negative feelings for you. Accept they did their best and let the feelings go. If you can, talk to them about it. You may be surprised to hear their perspective on the situation. Do not blame them; take responsibility for yourself and your reactions. If you find this difficult, the techniques described in Chapter Twenty may help you.

If you are a parent yourself, you have a huge responsibility. There is no such thing as perfect parenting, so do what you believe is right. It is good education for a child to realise that a parent can make mistakes, because this is part of being human. The most important thing in my opinion is to demonstrate your love and acceptance of them, even when they do things you disagree with or don't approve of. Treat your child as an independent individual with their own character and opinions, and not someone who belongs to you. You are entrusted with their upbringing when they are a child but you do not own them.

If you find yourself in a situation with lots of emotional turmoil, writing down the issues may help. Read back what you have written as a detached observer, treating the people involved and yourself as characters in a story. Taking a different perspective may help you to change your behaviours to improve or resolve the situation.

You don't know what is going on in other people's reality. They may feel guilty, inferior, or scared that you may show them up. They may think that what you are doing will cause you problems or unhappiness in the future and want to prevent you having to experience that. Perhaps they feel they have to keep you engaged in a battle with them to distract you from something they are doing or to stop you achieving the success they have been unable to attain. It can become like a game they are unaware they are playing. The people involved say or do something and they expect you to make your move and react in the way you always have. Refuse to play the game. If you change your tactics you may open up new possibilities. This is discussed in more detail in Chapter Eighteen.

I remember an incident when I was swimming in a pool and a lady complained loudly to a friend that I was splashing and making her wet. I was swimming; quite a normal thing to do in a swimming pool, I thought. She was just sitting at the end talking, apparently hoping to stay mostly dry. She had prepared the game board for conflict, perhaps unconsciously, so when I swam up to her and apologised she did not know how to react. I had broken the rules of the game by not pointing out that swimming generates splashes and makes people wet. I suspect that if I had played the game, she would probably have gone home and relayed the story about how she was innocently sitting beside the pool when a bully came and splashed her, then proceeded to argue with her for no reason.

It is equally possible that the other people involved have no idea that you are so upset by a specific situation. They may be acting in the only way they know how, or think they are doing you a favour. They may have their own issues and circumstances that they are locked into and unable to escape from. They may feel it is you who is being unreasonable. Parents in particular often believe they know better than their children and feel their advice should be accepted without question. This may have been true at one time, but not when their children have become adults.

You are only responsible for yourself and no other adult. If you are unhappy about something, it is up to you to resolve it. You cannot take responsibility if someone else is upset by what you decide to do; it is their choice to feel that way. Of course you do not want to deliberately upset someone you care about, but to do something you don't want to do just to keep them happy is being disrespectful to yourself and can create many problems.

Firstly, you don't know if your actions will make them happy because you can't control their feelings. Then if they don't appreciate that you have made a sacrifice, you may resent them. You may come to resent them anyway and hold them responsible for preventing you from following your desires, even though they may have had no idea what you really wanted. Communication is the key here. You must make your thoughts and feelings clear to avoid misunderstandings. You can be assertive without being disrespectful.

Assertiveness is really about honouring and respecting yourself. If you don't agree with something, make it known that this is the case. You don't have to provide an explanation. Your opinion is as important as anyone else's and you have a right to express it. Anyone who respects you will accept it, and if they don't respect you, you have to question their motives or their true feelings for you. Receiving respect from others starts with respecting yourself enough to value your opinions.

There may be situations where a joint decision is required on an important issue, but you and the others involved have different opinions. In a work situation you may have to decide on a plan of action, but everyone has different ideas about how to achieve it. In this case you must start with a common area of agreement. Usually this will be the high-level objective, such as increasing the sales of the company's product. Make sure you all acknowledge this agreement before continuing.

You can then all present your ideas and opinions and explore the advantages and disadvantages. Use the listening skills you have learnt and communicate your ideas clearly. You may eventually have to compromise, but this does not necessarily mean abandoning your values or changing your opinions. You can acknowledge another person has different views from you without agreeing with those views. If the majority decision is in contradiction to your opinion, you can make it known that you disagree but that you will support that decision and do what you can to make it work. Stay professional and do not allow emotions to interfere with working together on the task at hand.

One point I would like to make here is that it is OK to change your mind. Some people think they have to stick to their decision regardless of changing circumstances. The more flexible you are, the greater your ability to adapt to change. If on reflection you realise your decision was flawed, say so. Don't persist with something you recognise as unsuitable just on principle.

In intimate relationships emotions run high and it may not be so easy to keep to the guidelines above. We can probably learn the most from our partners and close family by noticing the way we react to them. When you know someone intimately, you have probably discussed your feelings and emotions, and know their likes and dislikes from experience. Don't let this trick you into making assumptions about exactly how they feel. You can never enter their reality or understand what they really feel. I keep repeating this because it is so important. Communicate with each other, but don't make assumptions.

A very common assumption is to think that you understand what your partner means when he or she says "I love you." Our personal understanding and experience of the feeling we call love is unique. The word love is often interpreted as an expression of absolute devotion. However, this does not mean that your partner will agree with all your opinions or share your goals for the future.

Some people misinterpret the feeling of having their needs met by someone else as love. They think that if they feel loved, wanted, or special in the presence of a particular person, it must be love. If you are relying on your needs being met externally, they will never be completely fulfilled. You are putting unreasonable demands on your partner and this may cause a strain on your relationship. You must love and accept yourself.

It is important to share your feelings to the best of your ability to avoid misunderstandings. People can have very different ideas about what a loving relationship means. To you it may mean sharing everything and having children, but your partner may want to retain some freedom and individuality, and might have no desire for children.

To make a relationship work, you need to have a certain level of maturity and to have your own identity. You need to be secure enough in yourself to share part of your life yet remain individual. Many people enter into intimate relationships because they want to merge with another person and feel this is the only way they can become complete. On a physical level we can never be complete in ourselves, which is one reason why so many people seek out a partner of the opposite sex.

On an emotional and spiritual level you can be complete in yourself and this is the goal your unconscious mind is continually seeking to achieve. The mistake many people make is thinking that a partner who has the qualities they lack can make them complete. Relying on someone else for the aspects of yourself that you don't have will not result in lasting fulfilment. I'm not saying you can't have a happy relationship with such a person, just that developing yourself to your full potential will be more fulfilling.

When you commit to a relationship with someone, you are accepting them as they are. They have their own values and standards, which may be different from yours. Don't expect them to give up parts of their personality such as interests, hobbies or beliefs, although they may choose to do this. Equally, don't give up parts of yourself without considering the consequences. At the start of a relationship you may want to spend every minute with your partner, but it is important to maintain your individuality and to leave space for you both to grow and change.

In an intimate relationship, you are sharing a part of your life with someone. Exposing aspects of yourself to someone else can be threatening and may make you feel vulnerable. You have to trust your partner not to exploit your vulnerability, and similarly you must respect the privacy of your partner and of the relationship.

You probably also have to share possessions, time and commitments. This can be a source of conflict if you have different goals or a different approach to life. Even if you communicate well and make your desires known, life will usually present some unforeseen challenges. It is at these times that you need to find an area of common agreement to work from. Remember you are a partnership working together to contribute to the happiness and success of yourselves and the relationship. Some compromise will be required.

I believe that trust, respect and honesty are vital to a stable relationship. Some may argue that it is not necessary to be honest at all times, and that bending the truth to protect your partner's feelings is kinder than total honesty. We have already established that you cannot fully understand someone else's reality, and that you do not actually cause their feelings, so your guess as to how to protect them may be incorrect. Dishonesty may cause more hurt and can often have unexpected repercussions.

Assuming that you spend a lot of time with your partner, there is a high probability that he or she will stimulate some of your old emotions. You need to have enough self-awareness to recognise when you are reacting based on an old pattern of behaviour. It is easy to blame your partner for making you feel the way you do, but you must own your feelings and emotions.

Similarly, it is likely that things you do and say will stimulate old emotions in your partner. If they react unreasonably to an innocent remark, realise that it is probably not what you said that caused the reaction, but their interpretation of it based on their reality. The best thing you can do in this situation is to remain calm. If you become defensive, you build up tension between you. Accept they have an unresolved issue that they need to come to terms with.

Do you know why you chose your partner (or best friend)? You may say you found them attractive, kind, supportive, intelligent, or you had shared interests. But there are probably hundreds of people who fit that description, so what was special about the person you chose? It is almost certain that you are unaware of many of the reasons because your unconscious mind was directing you. The unconscious communication between you revealed many things that you may still not be aware of.

Some of these are instinctual, as discussed in Chapter Fourteen. Indeed, many people say there was a certain chemistry between them, indicating some unspoken and unknown interaction.

The unconscious mind is not logical, and may associate unrelated attributes. For example, if your father was loving and caring and happened to have large ears, you may find yourself unconsciously drawn towards people with large ears. You may recognise that your partner or special friend shares certain physical characteristics with one of your parents.

It may be that you chose them specifically because they would help you stimulate unresolved issues. Although this may sound unromantic, if they help you overcome the issues, your life should be better as a result. So don't become annoyed at your partner's reactions or behaviours; recognise the opportunity to resolve your emotional baggage and be grateful to your partner for offering you the opportunity.

In order to make any relationship work, you have to compromise. You will never agree on everything, so at least one of you will have to give way. In a healthy relationship you will both be happy to compromise, and this may mean using some of the techniques described in Chapter Fifteen. You can support your partner without necessarily agreeing with them or sharing their opinions. Even if you don't feel you can support them, at least respect their wishes.

If the situation arises where one person is very negative about a certain course of action, I believe the other should not expect their partner to comply. A strong reaction against something could indicate an underlying fear, and fear is much stronger and more unpleasant than the mere disappointment of not doing something you want to. Love means accepting and respecting such feelings.

Resentments can build up over time. If there are frequent conflicts with your partner, you may have to change the rules of the game as described earlier. It may be that your partner is reacting in anticipation of what you may do or say, or that you are stimulating old emotions. Modify your reactions and observe the results. Use communication skills to ensure you are understood. It may take patience and perseverance to create the conditions that allow the resentments to dissolve.

If you resent a certain action or behaviour of your partner, recognise that they probably did not intend to upset you. Assume there was a misunderstanding and let the incident go. If you believe they deliberately set out to upset you, accept they have their own issues and they may have reacted out of fear. When it is appropriate, discuss your perceptions and feelings in a calm way. Aim to resolve the matter before any more resentments can build up.

Some people use confrontational behaviours as a test of love. They may feel insecure and want you to demonstrate your commitment. Their reality may be restrictive, and they may not realise there are other ways of behaving, or other ways to interpret your behaviour. You cannot resolve someone else's issues for them; they have to do that for themselves. Just accept they are at a certain level of emotional development and allow them to grow at their own rate. Love them as they are.

A common source of misunderstanding is a difference in the way you and your partner process information; a different primary representational system. You may think you are communicating clearly, but if you are not using the language your partner responds to, your message may not be getting through.

Consider this example. A man who is primarily kinaesthetic comes home from work after a hard day and relaxes on the sofa. His visual partner arrives home later after an equally hard day and notices the lounge is very untidy. She complains that he should have cleared up the mess as he was home earlier. He explains that he has had a very stressful day and just wanted to relax and feel comfortable – he is concerned about how he feels. She is angry and says, "But didn't you see all those piles of books? Didn't you look around you? Are you blind?" The visual aspects of his environment are less important to him, so he doesn't consciously notice them.

If you recognise the differences in the way you and your partner perceive the world, it will help you understand why things that are important or obvious to you may be insignificant to them, or vice versa. To improve your communication you can modify your language to use words that they are more likely to relate to. It may help to talk about what you are most aware of. For example, if you are primarily auditory, you may have to explain that you notice sounds more, and background noises are more irritating to you.

If your partner is kinaesthetic, recognise that he or she may talk slowly and leave longer gaps between phrases. Respect this in conversation and don't be tempted to use hesitation as an excuse to interrupt. This may be a particular challenge if you are primarily visual, and may be a test of your listening skills.

Patterns of behaviour, called metaprogrammes in NLP, can cause confusion in relationships. For example, if you think in terms of detail, but your partner tends to think about the topic in general, there may be some frustration. When choosing a car, you may have clear ideas about the engine size, safety aspects, boot capacity, and colour. You know you want air conditioning, leather seats and heated mirrors, but your partner may just want a reliable mode of transport. You can't determine exactly what your partner wants because he or she does not consider the detail in the same way that you do.

You may have a positive outlook on life but your partner may be more negative. You may think of the safety benefits and comfort of the car, whereas you partner is more aware of the running costs and depreciation. Understanding that you have different metaprogrammes can help you consider and understand each other's perspective better and allow the possibility of meeting somewhere in the middle.

Regardless of what society would like us to believe, men and women are different in the way they think and feel. Brain scanning technology has been used to determine which areas of the brain are stimulated when performing specific tasks. It has proved that, in general terms, men and women process certain information differently. The average female is more emotional, creative, multitasking, family oriented and is a better communicator compared with the average man. The average male is more aggressive, logical, sports oriented, has better spatial awareness and thinks about sex more than the average woman. These are biological traits, not just cultural stereotypes.

Awareness of these differences can help you understand your partner and friends better and allow you to work together using the skills best suited to each of you. Further research into this issue is a good investment for stronger, healthier relationships – see the Further Reading section for recommended books.

If you find that many of your relationships fail, remember that the thing that all your relationships have in common is you. You always take yourself into every relationship. If you have an attitude of "all men/women are the same", it could be an indication that it is you who need to change. Everyone is different, but your reaction to, or behaviour towards them may be the same. Some honest self-examination may be required to recognise what you must do to maintain a relationship.

It is through relationships that we learn about ourselves. Every interaction and every conflict is an opportunity to learn more. The emotions that are stimulated in you most often are the ones you need to understand and resolve. The things you find irritating or unpleasant in others are likely to be aspects of yourself that you have not acknowledged. Appreciate all your relationships as they have the potential to bring you inner peace and happiness.

Chapter 17

Presence

By presence, I mean being present in life and in the universe. We have already established that we live our lives in our minds, and that reality consists of the memories we have accumulated over the years. Some people spend a lot of their time in nostalgic reminiscing. Of course, it can be very enjoyable to remember an event from the past, reliving the excitement, pride or romance. But for some, living in the past becomes habitual. They are so engrossed in their memories that they miss what is going on in the present. New events only become interesting if they relate to their past reality.

Other people spend most of their time planning for the future and are always looking forward to something. It is good to make plans as long as this is balanced with enjoyment of the present. However, for some, the planning and dreaming means they miss what is happening in the present moment, in the now. There are also people who spend their time worrying about the future. They don't enjoy life to the full because they are always anticipating something bad that could happen in the future. Because they were not fully present at the time of an event, they can only enjoy it at a later time through their memories, thus losing some of the detail and enjoyment.

Worrying must be the most useless activity we can indulge in. I have heard some people say that if they don't have something to worry about they become agitated and worried! Worry is a negative activity which stresses the mind and body and drains energy. Intense and prolonged worrying creates so much stress that it has an adverse effect on health. I don't believe there are any benefits from worrying whatsoever.

If you have any control over the thing that worries you, take appropriate action to eliminate the source of the worry. For example, if it is an event, do everything you can to ensure it runs smoothly. If it is an exam, prepare yourself fully by studying and revising. (Chapter Twenty may be useful for enhancing your learning.) If it involves what someone else may do, discuss it with them if possible. It may be that you can't take action immediately. In this case, decide when you can, make a note of what you will do in your diary and then forget about it until this time.

Paradoxically, worrying engages the conscious mind so much that it can interfere with sensible thought processes and make the situation worse. You could be sitting in a traffic jam worrying about missing an appointment. Perhaps you are so wound up in your prediction of the consequences that it doesn't occur to you that you know a way to your destination on less busy roads. Your unconscious mind may have been trying to alert you to this, but your conscious mind was too preoccupied to recognise the message. And had you been more relaxed and focused on the present, you may have noticed a signpost or heard the suggested alternative route on the traffic report.

If you are worrying about something you don't have any control over, you're wasting your time and energy. Remember that your unconscious mind creates your reality based on your thoughts. It is therefore more productive to imagine the best outcome rather than concentrating on the negative possibilities. Worrying and thinking about all the terrible things that could happen increases the chances of them actually happening. You may wonder how this can be true if you have no control over the issue. There are two main reasons why this is so.

Firstly, if the issue is under the control or influence of someone else, it is quite likely that you will pass on your worry and negativity to them. Whenever you contact or interact with them, you will probably communicate your true feelings to them. Even if you try your best to be positive, it is likely that the other person will pick up your unconscious communication (as described in Chapter Twelve). They may have been positive and confident about the issue previously, but your negativity could cause doubt to enter their mind. This doubt could alter their thoughts and actions and influence the outcome, resulting in some of the negative things you were worried about.

Secondly, everyone and everything in the universe is connected. The universe is composed of atoms, and vibrating atoms create energy. Vibrating atoms are everywhere. You arc just a mass of vibrating atoms, as is the chair you are sitting on and the air above your head. It is the difference in the frequency of the vibrations that distinguishes what you recognise as different objects. The lower the frequency, the denser or more solid the object is. Even within your body, the atoms vibrate at different frequencies depending on where they are. Each of your organs has different vibrations. The atoms that make up your skin vibrate at a different frequency from those just below the surface and those in the air surrounding your body. So how do you determine where you 'end' and where the air around you or the chair you are sitting on 'begins'?

Some people can see the electromagnetic field around our bodies, called the aura, and it can also be photographed using special techniques. The quality, colour and size of your aura is affected by your health, thoughts and emotions. So is this part of you, or do you 'end' at your skin? What really separates you from everything else? The quality of your energy affects the area around your body in a similar way to the force of a magnet that either attracts or repels.

Everything you do affects your immediate environment in some way, and ultimately the universe. Every action causes a reaction, which causes another reaction. You are part of the whole. The vibrating mass of atoms you identify as you interacts with the atoms around you. You could consider yourself as just one cell in the body we call the universe, in the same way as your own body consists of millions of cells. Each cell in your body has a specific purpose and must work in harmony with the other cells in order to keep you healthy. It only takes one infected, damaged or over-active cell to affect your whole body. In the same way, your actions affect the universe.

So if you are constantly worrying about something, you are going to react in a certain way. Perhaps you don't concentrate fully on what you are doing in the present moment because of your preoccupation with the worrisome thoughts. Your actions are affected by your worry, and these actions can set off a chain of reactions. If you allow yourself to be distracted while driving or pouring boiling water into a cup, for example, you could put yourself or others in danger. In this case it is clear how you are allowing worry to influence your environment.

Just as your body is energy, so are your thoughts. Your thoughts change your vibrational energy, and therefore influence the whole. When many people share similar thoughts they can have a powerful effect. Directed prayer is an example of this being used in a positive way. However, if you are constantly worrying, you are sending negative vibrations into your environment.

Many people can detect thought vibrations and may talk about 'an air of anticipation' or 'an atmosphere of trust'. I have heard people say "You could cut the air with a knife", implying very low vibrations, which are the density of negative thoughts. We may say someone is 'on the same wavelength' or 'has bad vibes'. Some people even claim to be able to 'smell fear'. Perhaps others detect these energy vibrations on an unconscious level.

Entertainers and sports people will testify that an excited and supportive audience can be uplifting and help them to improve their performance. People who are part of the audience can be swept along by the feelings and find themselves shouting and chanting, which is normally out of character for them. They are being influenced by the collective thoughts of the crowd.

As the nature of your habitual thoughts affects you and your environment, it makes sense to hold as many positive thoughts as possible. Recognise that worrying about things in the future is not only counter-productive, but also detracts from your enjoyment of the present moment. Be aware that gossiping about other people also sets up negative vibrations. Even though you are talking about someone else and perhaps directing negativity towards them, those negative thoughts are originating from you and are affecting your environment. Thoughts of revenge, hatred or jealousy may well reflect back at you.

Experience everything to the full as it happens. The past has gone and is nothing more than a memory, and the future hasn't arrived yet and is only imagination. The place to be is the here and now. This is where the most enjoyment and happiness exists. Live in the moment. This is not the same as living *for* the moment, which can result in being reckless, inconsiderate and having no regard for others or the future.

If reliving the memory was as good as the actual experience, you wouldn't seek to experience it again. But you do – if you have enjoyed something before, you usually want to do it again. In fact the more enjoyable it was, the more motivated you are to repeat it, confirming that the pleasure is in the now. Conversely, if you were not fully present during the experience, your memory may be incomplete or distorted. You may find certain experiences much better or worse than the way you remembered them. This may be an indication that you need to give more attention to the present.

Enjoyment of the present moment is not something that receives much emphasis in our culture. Instead, we are encouraged to think ahead, plan for the future, save for a rainy day. As soon as we enter paid employment we are expected to start contributing to a retirement pension that we will not enjoy the benefits of for forty years or so. Although these things are not bad in themselves, they tend to set up a pattern, a habitual way of living that detracts from the present.

Our intellectual and technological society provides us with all sorts of entertainment, gadgets, literature and pastimes designed to stimulate our intellect. However, the key to enjoying the now is to attend to your feelings. Feelings come from the body as opposed to thinking, which is centred in the head. In order to stay present you must feel more and think less – turn off the internal dialogue inside your head. There are many ways you can achieve this.

A good way to start is to become aware of what is happening in your immediate environment. Whenever you are doing something that doesn't demand your constant conscious attention, take the opportunity to just look around and notice all the details that perhaps you may have ignored before. Interesting shapes, textures and patterns of light can usually be found even in apparently uninteresting surroundings. Be aware of sounds, the sensations of your body, your breathing. Don't pass judgement on anything, just notice these things. You can do this for a few seconds or a few minutes at a time, depending on circumstances.

At first you will probably find your mind protesting, suggesting this is a waste of time, or that you have more important things to do. You may catch yourself thinking about what you will be doing tomorrow or remembering your last conversation with your boss. Just bring your awareness back to the present and to your feelings. At this precise moment you have everything you need, so just relax and enjoy it. The pressures of life can wait. Don't allow yourself to be so engrossed in the past or the anticipation of the future that you miss the beauty of now.

It can be very beneficial to set aside times during the day specifically for quieting the mind. Anything that helps you become more aware of your body and your feelings is good. This could be a relaxing bath, a massage, yoga, listening to and allowing yourself to become absorbed in music, or meditation.

There are many forms of meditation and you may have to experiment to find what works best for you. I recommend meditating once or twice a day, preferably at around the same times, as this can encourage your mind to become accustomed to the process. If your schedule does not allow this, take whatever opportunities you can. Choose a quiet place where you will not be disturbed or distracted. You can listen to soft, calming music if you find it deepens your meditation.

Sit in a comfortable position with your spine straight. If this is impossible or uncomfortable, you can lie down, but I believe sitting allows a better flow of energy throughout your body. As we have already discovered, your posture and body language can affect your mind, so relax physically as much as possible to encourage calmness in your mind. Some people find that concentrating on relaxing each of the muscle groups in turn is helpful. I prefer starting at the toes and working up to the head. If you have difficulty relaxing your body, it may help to tense the muscles and then notice the feeling of release when you relax them.

When you are as physically relaxed as you can be, deepen the relaxation of your mind. There are numerous ways to do this and you may need to experiment to find what works best for you. For example, you could count slowly from five down to one, imagine walking down a staircase, surround yourself with white light, imagine you are in a lift going down, feel yourself sinking into the chair, or imagine you are becoming very small. Whichever method you choose, use the same one every time so that your mind becomes accustomed to the process and learns to enter deep relaxation quickly.

Most disciplines use the principle of focusing your attention on one thing to prevent your mind from wandering and going back into thinking mode. This could be an image, a sound, which is usually called a mantra, or a feeling. You can use your knowledge of how you tend to process information (with a visual, auditory or kinaesthetic bias) to guide you towards what may work best for you.

One visual approach is to stare at an object, such as the flame of a candle. Personally I don't advocate this because of the damage that staring can have on the visual system, as described in Chapter Seven. Even holding a single image in your mind encourages mental staring, and as imagination is an important aspect of vision, it can still be detrimental to the eyes. I believe visualising a relaxing scene is a more effective way of inducing a calm state of mind.

Auditory approaches use a word such as 'relax' or 'calm' or a mantra specially chosen for you. You continuously repeat this in your mind throughout the duration of your meditation. You may find this method works for you if your thoughts are often dominated by internal dialogue; a voice inside your head. Repeating the word helps to stop any other mental chatter intruding. However, if your thoughts are mainly images or feelings, this approach may not be enough to stop your mind straying from the mantra.

My favoured methods of meditation are kinaesthetically based. This means devoting your attention to a specific part of the body, a particular feeling or an emotion. What I recommend is to concentrate on your breathing, noticing every detail of the breath going in and out of your body. You could also imagine roots extending from your feet into the ground to enhance your connection with the earth. Bringing your attention into your body promotes awareness and can guide you towards the stillness that resides within you, a place of peace and happiness.

Spend about half an hour in meditation or relaxation. If your goal is general stress relief, self-awareness or to become more connected to the oneness of the universe, allow your mind to clear. If you notice your mind wandering from the image, mantra or feeling you are concentrating on, gently bring your attention back to it. With some practice this becomes easier, and you may find that all thoughts just drop away. Enjoy the emptiness that remains. It can be tempting to get excited at this point and think "Wow, I've reached the point of stillness inside", but of course this will have reactivated your mind!

You may find that feelings or emotions surface for no apparent reason. Just notice them and allow them to flow away or disperse. If some of them are intense or persistent, they may be unresolved issues that are being presented to you for resolution and release. This is an ideal safe environment to work with them as described in previous chapters. Feel them fully and focus your attention on them. They may change, evolve or move, so just give the process time.

Your unconscious mind is more open to suggestion in the meditative or deeply relaxed state. You can use the techniques described above to enter this state and then visualise your desires, as described in Chapter Twelve. Remember to add as much sensory detail (colours, movement, sounds, feelings, textures) as possible to make the process more powerful. Imagine your goal from your own perspective, as if looking through your own eyes. If you have a tendency to dissociate from the scene, that is you see yourself in the picture as an observer as opposed to being immersed in it, imagine yourself stepping into the 'you' that you can see. Feel yourself become part of the action. The more real it seems to you, the more effective the process is likely to be.

While you are deeply relaxed, you can ask for guidance on particular issues, or seek solutions or insights into your problems. The principles are the same as those described Chapter Nineteen.

Deep relaxation is also a good way to embark on self-hypnosis. While your mind and body are relaxed, you can give yourself suggestions, either in the form of affirmations or internal dialogue. I recommend preparing a script in advance so that you can choose your words carefully. As we have already explored, the exact words and phrases you use to communicate with your unconscious mind are very important. Follow the same rules of always using positive statements and adding plenty of sensory detail. If your script is too long to remember, you can record it on tape or CD to play during your sessions.

Even if you believe you don't have time for regular relaxation or meditation sessions, there are simple exercises you can do, some taking less than a minute to complete. Just focusing on your breathing for a few seconds can be helpful. An exercise I recommend is to imagine you are breathing in the loving vibrations all around you and breathing out all negativity. You can enhance this by further imagining you are breathing through all the pores in your body.

A more visual version of this is to imagine pure white light entering your body through your head and filling every nerve and every cell so that you glow with purity and love. As you do this you may feel a tingling in your hands and fingers as the energy flows through you.

The energy that flows through you and all living things is sometimes called the life force, or 'chi'. There are seven main energy centres in the body called chakras. These are spinning horizontal discs of coloured light, as illustrated in Figure 1. The root chakra spins clockwise in men and anti-clockwise in women. The direction of spin of the other chakras then alternates right up to the crown.

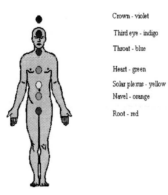

Crown - violet

Third eye - indigo

Throat - blue

Heart - green

Solar plexus - yellow

Navel - orange

Root - red

Figure 1. Location, names and colours of the chakras

To re-energise and help ground yourself, imagine the chakras spinning. Start with the root chakra and imagine a red disk spinning in the area of your coccyx. Then imagine an orange disk spinning in the opposite direction just below your navel and so on up through to your crown. When you have done this, imagine each disk folding up like the petals of a flower. So starting with the crown chakra, imagine the violet disk folding, then the indigo disk of the third eye, and so forth down to the root chakra, until they are all closed. You can do this in twenty seconds.

Another way to encourage presence is to appreciate your life and experiences. You can practise gratitude at any time. You have plenty of things to be grateful for; your health, freedom, the people in your life, your attributes, skills, possessions, and many, many other things. Even when the situation seems to be going badly, reflect on the good things in your life. At the end of every day before going to sleep, express your gratitude to the universe for the events that happened during the day, the kindness people demonstrated towards you, what you achieved, the insights or lessons you learnt and all the things you normally

165

take for granted.

When you live in the moment and pay more attention to your feelings, you are more likely to notice any communication from your unconscious mind. You may decide to do something based on your intuition. This encourages synchronicity, which is where an apparently random set of circumstances opens up new opportunities for you or enables you to resolve a problem. When you express gratitude to the universe, as discussed above, you may find that people and events seem to be working in your favour. This is because you are creating an environment of trust and harmony.

An example of synchronicity happened to me several years ago. I had an appointment in London and had planned my train journey and booked the taxi to the station. The taxi was late arriving at my house, and I missed the train I had intended to catch. I caught the next train and spent the first part of the journey angry with the taxi driver and anxious that I would be late for my appointment. Then the train stopped. Its path was blocked by a terrible accident at Clapham involving the train that I had missed. The incident claimed over thirty lives and left many others injured. I was suddenly very grateful to the taxi driver and whatever the circumstances were that caused him to be delayed.

Situations that seem negative at the time can actually turn out to be beneficial to you, so always appreciate what is happening to you and keep an open mind. If you think that events are consistently working against you or causing you problems, examine the situations as a detached observer. In this way you may be able to determine a pattern in your behaviour or attitudes, or recognise a message from your unconscious mind.

A concept that can be very useful to help you live in the now involves recognising the location of your 'time line'. If you had to imagine a line that consists of all the events of your life in chronological order, where would it be? Some people feel this imaginary line runs through them from front to back, with the past behind them and the future in front of them. NLP calls this being 'in time'. They often talk of leaving the past behind and looking forward to the future. Others imagine the line is in front of them, with the past to the left and the future to the right, called 'through time'. There are other possibilities, but these are the most common perceptions.

Those who process their time line in the 'through time' configuration have the advantage of being able to 'see' all their life events easily because they are in front of them. They may be more organised and disciplined than their 'in time' counterparts. However, they are usually detached from their time line, rarely actually in the moment. It is as if they are observing their life rather than actually being part of it. This time line is often associated with the precision and restrictions of Western culture.

Those with an 'in time' configuration tend to be more relaxed and have more presence because they are always part of their time line, immersed in the now. It could be argued that 'in time' people are less likely to learn from their experiences because the past is behind them, possibly forgotten. It may also be that they have fewer regrets and are more easily able to leave the past behind them. It is my opinion that 'in time' people have the capacity to enjoy life more because they tend to experience life more intensely.

It can be very interesting to experiment with your time line. In a safe environment, stand up and imagine where your time line is. Then, leaving your imaginary time line in the same location, step to one side, step onto or off it, or turn around. Perhaps sink deeper into it or float above it. Allow yourself to feel the sensations associated with each position. If you find a configuration that feels better, you may want to adopt it. Or you may choose different configurations depending on circumstances. This can be a surprisingly powerful exercise.

Presence is what living is all about. We are human beings, designed to 'be'. The pace of modern life encourages us to be always active, always busy, always striving to achieve, more like 'human doings'. You have the choice of being in the moment or letting it pass you by.

Chapter 18

Contribution

As we explored in the previous chapter, your thoughts and actions can influence your environment and the people around you. You could consider yourself part of a system, and the way you behave within it has an effect on the whole. In fact, you are part of many systems.

For example, a family is a system. The members of a family have a particular role within it, and while everybody continues to fulfil their role, the system will function in broadly the same way. Roles may include a breadwinner, a decision-maker, an organiser, a housekeeper, a child-minder and a financial controller. Individuals may have several roles, or responsibility in some areas may be shared. There may be many other roles that are not so clearly defined, or that are not even recognised until they disappear. Each individual makes their contribution to the family, and as a result, the family unit may become greater and stronger than the sum of its parts.

If one part of the system suddenly changes, the whole system has to adapt, or it may break down. If the major breadwinner is made redundant, the main source of income to the system is removed, and the other members of the family have to either alter their spending habits or contribute more to the family finances. When a member leaves the system, such as an offspring leaving to set up home independently, it can cause major upheaval for the whole family. What may appear to you to be a minor change in your behaviours or your attitudes may cause significant changes to the system. Consider carefully the possible effects of your actions so that you can avoid, or at least prepare for, any negative repercussions.

In families, as in most systems, there are certain expectations and aspects that are taken for granted. Children are rarely aware of all the effort and organisation required to provide and maintain their home environment, or the planning and expense involved in their education. Problems can arise if one member of the family decides they no longer want to be taken for granted, and stop performing part of their role. This usually happens if they feel they are not appreciated. The disruption to the family can be high, and the other members may be perplexed and indignant. The best way to avoid this situation is to acknowledge and show gratitude for everyone in the family, no matter how small their contribution may seem.

You have an active involvement in many systems. If you work for a company, everything you do in the course of your work has the potential to affect the company and everyone who is part of it. It is tempting to think that in large companies your influence is negligible and that nothing you think, say or do will make any difference. This is a rather negative attitude that could lead to the downfall of the company, as discussed below, and subsequently the loss of your job and your income. This could affect the other systems that you are part of, such as your family. I know many people who steal from their employers. They think nothing of taking items of stationery or equipment for their personal use. They may justify this by saying that the cost of the items is insignificant in relation to the company's profits and it becomes acceptable behaviour to them. Or they say it makes up for extra hours they have worked, conveniently forgetting how much time they have taken off for medical or personal reasons, or the amount of time they spend on extended tea breaks. Stealing from your employer is an offence, and the more people who engage in the practice, the greater damage it will do to the company, to the system and ultimately, to you.

According to a recent report, over half of UK employees take time off as sick leave when they are not really ill. This apparently happens most often on days when there are major sporting events. They are using their sick leave entitlement as a way of acquiring more paid holiday. This practice has a high cost to industry and may affect your company's profits and therefore your pay and your job security. Respect and appreciate your employer and do not abuse the trust placed in you.

I have worked for large companies in which many of my colleagues felt that they were insignificant and that their particular area of work had little impact on the overall performance of the company. When the project on which they had worked very hard did not receive much attention, they felt they lacked the recognition and respect they deserved. This usually meant they put less effort into their next project, believing that it was not worth it because they would not be rewarded for it. You can probably appreciate that it only takes a small proportion of the workforce to hold these opinions to have an adverse effect on the whole project. I believe you should always put maximum effort into all the projects that you are involved with.

When my colleagues claimed they were not rewarded for their work, they neglected to remember the salary that they were paid, regardless of their performance. Because their payslip arrived every month, it became an expectation. They no longer recognised it as a form of appreciation, despite the fact that they were paid well, allowing them and their families to maintain a comfortable lifestyle. Even if you consider your wage to be low, it is important you recognise that you are being rewarded for your work, and therefore I believe you should always make the best contribution you can. The recent rise in industrial action in the UK, with workers demanding greater compensation, is an indication that those people do not recognise this concept and do not appreciate their jobs. Few people really appreciate their employment until they no longer have it. There is much more to a job than just the money, including purpose, shared values, relationships, recognition, teamwork, identity, status and social aspects. As discussed in Chapter Twelve, the more you appreciate the things you have in life and express your gratitude, the happier you will become.

For most people, the job they do is their major contribution to society because of the amount of time spent at their place of work. The more you enjoy your job, the more likely you are to do it well and make a significant contribution. In many social systems status is important, and status is often judged by profession, salary, or position within a company. Some people choose their jobs by these 'rules', despite the fact that they don't enjoy their job, or have to work in an unhealthy environment. You don't have to play by these rules. Perhaps you think that you have to earn a high salary to provide for your family, but they would probably rather accept a lower standard of living than watch you killing yourself through your highly stressful, well-paid job. You may find the information in Chapter Fourteen useful to determine your true motivations if you are pursuing a career that is less than ideal. You will make a much greater contribution if you commit to the work you love and that is consistent with your values.

Another system you are part of is your community. Many people are reluctant to become involved in community activities, preferring to leave it up to others. They may be quick to complain if the area is untidy, for example, but will not take part in a local clean-up day. They are, however, very happy to enjoy the benefits of community projects. If you walk down the road you live in and see a piece of litter on the ground, do you pick it up? I think most people would leave it there for the local council or somebody else to deal with. And as so many people adopt this attitude, the litter accumulates, blows around, attracts rodents and generally has a detrimental effect on the neighbourhood. What a difference it would make to the area if everyone contributed by picking up any litter they see – everyone would have less to complain about and would be a little happier, and the council could concentrate on providing more important services.

Most of us are part of the road transport system. The system has rules that must be adhered to if it is to be successful. We all understand which side of the road to travel on, what to do at junctions, etc. You must respect the rules in order to make travelling by road safe and effective. If you break the rules, such as jumping traffic lights or overtaking in a dangerous situation, the consequences could be disruptive or even fatal. The way you drive and behave in traffic affects everyone else travelling in the vicinity, and other drivers' actions affect your journey. You are all interacting within the same system.

On busy motorways, some motorists become inconsiderate, sometimes out of frustration, and pull out prematurely, switch from lane to lane in an effort to get a few cars ahead, or perform other dangerous manoeuvres. This often causes vehicles to brake, producing a cascade effect in the following traffic. When drivers do not leave a safe distance between them and the vehicle in front (which is, sadly, very common) sudden braking can cause accidents, disrupting the journey for thousands of other drivers. It is possible that if you drive inconsiderately, you could be starting a chain of events that lead to an accident behind you that you may not be aware of. Your actions could contribute to the death or injury of other motorists. Think of this next time you are in heavy traffic, and always drive safely and sensibly regardless of the situation. Is your appointment really so important that it is worth risking your own or someone else's life for? You may feel like an individual driving to your destination, but remember you are part of the road network system. Drive with consideration for the whole system.

You are part of the economy. A healthy economy relies on money circulating all the time. I am sure most people understand this concept, but it seems that many do not make the connection that they are a vital part of the economy and that they should willingly pay for the things they want or need. You have to spend money in order to keep the economy buoyant and to keep the companies you buy products and services from in business. If they go out of business, you suffer because you can't acquire whatever it was you wanted from them.

Some people will do whatever they can to avoid parting with their money, including bartering, making false claims and abusing warranties. I know people who have made false or exaggerated insurance claims, thinking that they are making a financial gain. However, what happens is that the insurance company has to increase its premiums to cover the fraudulent claims of its customers. The same people who thought they were benefiting from the situation end up paying more to insure their possessions in the future. They also increase the premiums for all the other customers of that company. In other words, they are abusing the system and affecting themselves and everyone else in it. Remember this if you have ever considered trying to get more than you are genuinely entitled to in any situation.

I recall a conversation between two of my friends. One was explaining how his local chip shop gave portions of chips so large that he couldn't finish them. To avoid wastage, he always requested a smaller amount, even though he was still charged the full portion price. The other, who frequented the same chip shop, said that she also found the portions too big, but took the whole amount because she had paid for it, and threw away the surplus. He was saying that this was silly, but she was emphatic that she was entitled to what she had paid for.

There are two points to this story. Firstly, if everyone asked for smaller portions, the shop might realise that the size was unsuitable and offer a smaller portion for a lower price. Secondly, if everyone requested smaller portions, there would be more chips to be circulated amongst the customers, and the shop would make a greater profit. This might result in them reducing their prices, or delaying a price increase. Both scenarios would benefit all the people in this system, that is, all the customers and the shop owners. The person who insisted on taking the complete portion was thinking only of herself and not recognising that her behaviour could be contributing negatively to the system (keeping prices higher than necessary). And as she was part of the system, the results of her negative actions would affect her too.

Many people resent the amount of tax they have to pay. They feel that they should be able to keep more of their hard-earned money. It is usually these same people who demand the state provides higher pensions, more amenities, better healthcare, safer communities and a higher standard of education, among other things. They apparently don't realise that they are part of the state, and that they provide the money for the state-funded facilities through their taxes. A more positive attitude would be to recognise the contribution you are making to the health and welfare of the system (the state), which includes you, your family and loved-ones. With this attitude, you are more likely to do things that are beneficial to the system, rather than thinking of ways to avoid contributing to it.

There are situations where people have made financial or other losses and expect compensation from the government. When they receive compensation, they think they have gained personally from it, not recognising that the billions of pounds

173

paid out in compensation claims have to be recovered from somewhere, usually through taxes. The term 'government money' that I hear so many people use, is a way of making it something external, some sort of pot of gold that mysteriously gets filled from an unknown source. Of course, we are all part of this system termed government money. We all contribute to it and we all benefit from the services the money provides.

The important issue in all the systems you belong to is personal responsibility. If you make a financial decision that does not reap the rewards you hoped for, take responsibility for that decision. Don't expect everyone else in the system to have to pay for your loss or your misguided judgement. Accept you may have made a mistake and learn from the experience. Any financial loss you have made goes back into the economy to help keep it healthy, and will eventually benefit you in some way. Remember that you create your own reality, so if things don't go according to plan it is your perceptions that need to change.

If everyone held a more positive attitude towards their contribution to society, it would make it better for us all. Take responsibility for your own health and well-being to avoid unnecessary drain on the health services. Treat the environment with respect, minimising waste and using environmentally-friendly products and practices. For example, if you have babies, weigh up the convenience of using disposable nappies with the fact that they are highly toxic and take nearly 500 years to decompose, therefore creating severe landfill and toxicity problems for over twenty generations into the future. With eight million of these nappies being disposed of *every day* in the UK alone, every time you use and dispose of one, you contribute to this enormous problem and your actions cause damage to the environment in which you and your family live.

Take responsibility for your involvement in every system you are part of and aim to make a positive contribution to them all. Recognise that your attitudes and behaviours within the system will affect you in some way. Treat others as you would like to be treated yourself and this will be reflected back to you in a favourable way. Use the information in Chapter Sixteen to forge positive relationships in all aspects of your life.

Most systems have a set of rules or guidelines to which all the members are expected to adhere. Sometimes the rules are unspoken, as in a family, where certain roles are assumed either by cultural stereotypes, habit or convenience. The system will continue to function in much the same way as long as the people within it interact in the same way. There may be a reasonable amount of order while children respect their parents, but if they become rebellious, the system can be thrown into turmoil.

One way to restore order to a system, or change it for the better, is to modify the way you react. For example, if you have been nagging your teenager to tidy her room, but it remains as untidy as ever, the rules become 'you nag, she ignores you'. The situation will stay the same as long as you both use these rules. You could change the rules by stating that if the mess is not cleared up by a certain date; you will throw away anything that is left on the floor. Make this new rule clear, and follow through with your part if necessary. If you don't throw away any clutter as agreed, or you extend the deadline, you are breaking the new rule and affirming the old rules. You must realise that you are contributing to the unwanted behaviour by tolerating it. Change your reactions and the behaviour of others will follow.

In work settings, there can be tension because several members of a team are competing for promotion or fighting for superiority in some way. One tactic they may use is to belittle the other team members, fail to recognise their contribution, or even sabotage the efforts of the others. The rules may become 'dog eat dog', in other words; each person is determined to come out on top, regardless of the negative effect on other individuals or the team goals. If you find yourself in this position, change your reactions and your attitude. Instead of finding ways to be better than the others, find ways to all work together. When your associate proposes a better solution than the one you presented, support it rather than defending yours. If your first method doesn't work, try another. You are part of the system, and with patience you can improve the way it functions.

If you find yourself having frequent arguments in personal relationships, change the way you react. Instead of insisting on putting your point across, keep it to yourself. Listen to the other person's opinion and choose if you want to accept or reject it. Let go of the need to be right, or if you can't do that, just know in your mind that you are right without insisting that others accept your opinion. You have changed the rules by refusing to join the argument. The other person can't argue on their own!

The challenge for us all is to release the obsession with selfish pursuits and personal gain. Do everything to the best of your ability, even if you think you will not receive any direct reward for your efforts. You are part of the whole, and your actions in every situation will eventually affect everyone and everything in some way. Next time you feel angry with someone or think you have been treated unfairly, remember that you are part of the same system. In most cases, the more you complain or try to retaliate, the more you disrupt the system for yourself and everyone else in it. You can choose how you react, and your choices will make a difference. Recognise that your contribution to the whole ultimately contributes to your own health and happiness.

Chapter 19

Dreams

Dreams can be an invaluable source of insight because they come directly from your unconscious mind. Your conscious mind is sleeping and cannot interfere or try to rationalise the messages your unconscious mind is sending. We all have dreams every night and, with a little practice, you can train yourself to remember many of them. The more interest you have in your dreams, the more likely your unconscious mind is to use this as a method of communicating with you.

One of the purposes of sleeping is to allow your mind to sort and store the experiences of the day, and some of this material may be reflected in your dreams. However, just because you recognise objects, scenes or people from the day's events does not mean that the dream is insignificant. I believe all dreams contain a useful message, although it may not always be easy to decipher.

A good way to start to recall your dreams is to say to yourself just before falling asleep "I want to remember my dreams." This technique was successful for me and I would wake up several times in the night after dreaming. After the novelty had worn off, this became a bit tedious, so I modified the phrase to "I want to remember my dreams clearly in the morning." You could also add "...after sleeping peacefully" or whatever you feel is appropriate. Remember that your unconscious mind takes your instructions literally. If you repeatedly claim you "never remember your dreams", this instruction will probably be accepted and obeyed.

If you don't remember your dreams on the first night you try this, don't immediately abandon your efforts. It may take practice and perseverance. Indicate your commitment to your unconscious mind by putting a pen and paper beside your bed to record the dreams as soon as you wake up. Better still, buy a notebook, label it 'Dream Journal' and put it by your bed.

I recommend keeping a journal of all your dreams, as this

can help you learn the meaning of the symbols and metaphors your mind presents to you. Sometimes dreams can form a series but may not necessarily come on consecutive nights. Keeping a log of previous dreams can help you to make such connections.

The memory of dreams can fade very quickly. Even dreams that are vivid and clear as you wake up can slip away. This is because the sleeping state is a different level of consciousness from waking, and communicating between the two states can present a challenge. You may find that just turning over to write causes the memory to disappear. If this happens often, stay in the same position to review the main points of the dream and compose a few phrases in your head to summarise it. This will help you retain it long enough to write it down. If your circumstances permit, you could say the phrases out loud before moving. This has the advantage that your conscious mind can hear your words, which should help with recall. If the dream fades as you move, reverting back to the original position may allow you to access it again.

There are products available that claim to assist in dream recall such as dream-catchers or crystals. Dreams are essentially thoughts and, as we learnt in Chapter Seventeen, these are energy vibrations. As all objects are also made up of vibrating energy, it seems quite feasible to me that the vibration of these products could influence the immediate environment and encourage and stimulate dreaming.

When you have remembered a dream, you can start to interpret it. I am generally not in favour of using dream dictionaries that give meanings for objects and events. The contents of your dreams are personal, based on your own experiences and private reality. Even symbols that have a universal general meaning or a particular cultural significance can have different interpretations in the context of the dream. I recommend you discover the language of your dreams for yourself using the techniques described below.

My preferred method of recording dreams is using two columns. In the left column write short phrases that describe each aspect of the dream. Keep the description exactly as you remember it without judging, censoring or analysing it. Use the present tense, as though you are still in the dream. This column represents the dream from the perspective of the unconscious mind. In the right column put your conscious interpretations of the phrases. Put the date you went to bed against each dream, even if you think it occurred in the early hours of the morning.

The rules of waking life and the laws of physics do not apply in dreams – dogs may talk, people may fly, time is not always linear, bizarre situations can seem normal. The unconscious mind communicates using symbols and metaphors, so the actual events in dreams are not necessarily meant to be taken literally. Your mind creates all the resources you need for the dream reality in order to convey the desired message.

An image can contain a great deal of information. If you dream of a talking dog, consider what a dog means to you. For example, it could represent a best friend, a pet, comfort, an inconvenience, animal instincts, fear, obedience or many other possibilities, depending on your own experience and opinion of dogs. The type of dog and its temperament could also be significant. If it was snarling, it could represent aggression; if scruffy it could mean untidiness or lack of care.

Include all the attributes of the image in the left column if you are using my suggested method above, and then your conscious interpretations of those attributes to the right. Some images create a metaphor that may not be obvious until you write the description. I once dreamt of my mother driving a car, which was unusual because she cannot drive in real life. For me, a car or other form of transport represents my journey through life. When I wrote down "My mother is in the driving seat" I realised the message was that I was allowing my life to be influenced by what I thought my mother would think of my actions.

The dream may include word play. So, for example, if you dream you are in a tent, it could be that you are intent on something. Dreaming of being surrounded by sea could mean there is a lot around you to see. Dreaming of a book could be reminding you to book an appointment.

If you can't make a logical interpretation of the phrases you have written down, just write the first idea that comes to you.

The unconscious mind is not logical, and thinking too deeply about the meaning may be blocking the message. If nothing comes to mind, leave it a while and you may find that the answer pops up when you least expect it. Otherwise, trust that your unconscious mind will send the message again in another form or another dream if it is important. Avoid asking someone else for their interpretation – you want to know what the message means for you, not for someone else.

Sounds in dreams can be relevant. If music is playing, does the tune have special significance for you? Do you regard it as happy, sad, invigorating or calming? Does the voice sound like someone familiar, even though it appears to be coming from a stranger? My dreams are predominantly visual, so when I had a dream that was just a voice saying "Eat live yogurt" I thought it must be significant. I believed myself to be healthy and wasn't aware of any symptoms related to an imbalance of intestinal flora. However, I trusted that my unconscious mind knew what was best for me so I followed the advice and incorporated bio-yogurt into my diet.

As the unconscious mind is primarily concerned with keeping you healthy, it is quite likely that the messages will concern your health in some way, either physically or emotionally. They may be encouraging you to adopt a healthier lifestyle, warning you of the effects of your current thoughts or actions, or indicating a more balanced attitude towards an aspect of your life.

Feelings are a very important aspect of dreams. Sometimes a dream can leave you with a feeling that does not seem appropriate to its contents. Perhaps you were being attacked by a tiger but felt very calm. In this case I believe the feeling is at least as important as the rest of the dream. One interpretation might be that there is no need to panic, as everything will be OK. Your analysis of the image of the tiger might reveal the situation about which you can relax.

You may have the reverse effect where you feel strong emotion for no apparent reason. This could be telling you there is more to the situation represented by the dream than may be immediately apparent. When I receive dreams like this I thank my unconscious mind for the warning and do my best to relate the dream scenario to my current or future life events.

Your body reacts to feelings and emotions in dreams as if they were real. This is why you may wake up from a nightmare sweating and with your heart pounding with fear. If you are not aware of any feelings associated with a dream, noticing any physical reactions when you wake up may give you a clue as to what they were.

Occasionally, you may not be able to remember a dream but are left with some vague impression of it, or you have a feeling for which you do not know the source. It is worth recording this because it may be relevant to previous or later dreams. Events of the day may trigger other memories of the dream.

Sometimes dream interpretations only make sense when you examine all the dreams with a similar theme. Dreams that are set in a particular location, or with the same group of people, or featuring a specific object or feeling, may be part of a series. You may have to review them all to understand the overall message.

I usually assume that the people and objects are offering me messages, and I interpret the meaning based on how they affect me. Another method is to interpret the dream from the perspective of every character and object in it. Your unconscious mind created them all, so it is reasonable to assume it had some idea of the attributes associated with them. In the tiger example above, you could consider the dream from the tiger's perspective. For example, perhaps there is somebody in your life who is fearful and feels the need to attack you in order to defend themself.

Recurring dreams are highly significant. Your unconscious mind is so keen to convey a very important message to you that it keeps repeating it until you take appropriate action. Years ago, before I knew about the power of dreams, I often dreamt I was in a dark house and when I turned the light on the bulb would blow or the switch wouldn't work. I would go around the whole house, but none of the lights would stay on, so I was in the dark and frightened. At the time I thought there must be some relevance to the frequency of the dream, and mentioned it to several people, but nobody suggested it was important.

I now believe it was a message to look after my eyesight. I used to spend all my working days in front of a computer, and after several years of this, I became short-sighted. It was at this time that I stopped having this dream. I am now able to interpret it knowing that to me, a house represents my body, and in the darkness I could not see. Also, fear is often a contributing factor in visual defects, and can indicate there is something we don't want to see or are scared to look at. This concept is discussed in Chapter Twenty-one.

Your unconscious mind can provide you with ideas or solve problems while you sleep. You may find you wake up in the night with inspiration or a solution, in which case I strongly recommend you write it down immediately. You may be fortunate enough to remember it in the morning, but it may slip away as dreams do. I believe that many examples of creativity and answers to problems are presented in dreams, but go unnoticed. To benefit from such information you have to remember and interpret the dreams.

You can specifically ask for guidance on particular issues, or seek solutions or insights into your problems. The source of the answers is open to debate, but popular beliefs include your unconscious mind, divine intelligence, the universe, the collective unconscious, God, spirit, or your higher consciousness. There is a philosophy behind each of these beliefs, and I will leave you to investigate those that interest you and draw your own conclusions. Regardless of what you believe, the answers do come, and they come via your unconscious mind.

How you ask the questions is important. Firstly, select just one issue to work with to avoid confusion. Phrase the question in such a way that it reduces the chances of ambiguities in the response. If you ask "Why do I keep getting used?" there could be a whole host of reasons, and that could make communicating the answer to you complicated. A direct question, phrased positively, such as "What must I do to be respected?" is likely to receive a clearer response.

Address the question to whomever or whatever you think

you are communicating with. If you have no idea about this entity, you can just say "I want to know what I must do to be respected." The answer may come in a dream that night, or a few nights later. If you haven't received or haven't recognised the answer within a week, repeat the process, perhaps rephrasing the question to make it clearer. Remember the response will probably be symbolic or metaphoric.

The answer may be presented to you during your waking hours, so be alert to possible messages, as described in Chapter Twelve. If you have difficultly remembering or interpreting your dreams, you can induce a dream-like state for exploring issues. You can use one of the techniques described in Chapter Seventeen to induce deep relaxation, then ask direct questions or use creative visualisation.

To get the most from creative visualisation, relax your body fully and imagine yourself in a comfortable, relaxing place. Imagine all the details of the scene to make it as real as possible. You can then ask the question to whomever you feel is appropriate. You can imagine people you trust, a wise, old sage or whomever you like entering the scene. Allow the action to unfold as in a dream and be alert to signs. If you have had a dream where you thought you were about to receive an important message but you woke up too soon, you can use visualisation to recreate the dream environment as closely as possible and then allow the dream to run to completion.

Dream interpretation is a tool that can be used in conjunction with other methods of communicating with your unconscious mind. The more you use it, the better it will serve you. It is an excellent way of harnessing some of the power of your unconscious mind.

Chapter 20

Memory

As we have already explored, your life is all in the mind and your reality is formed from your memories. Therefore, the quality of your memory can have a direct impact on your life. Having a good memory can do a lot more for you than just help you remember facts more easily. You draw on memories to make decisions, so the more relevant and related memories you can recall, the more informed your decision is likely to be. A good memory can lead to a more organised life, allowing you to give your attention to the things that are important to you.

Short-term memory, which is mainly concerned with sensory perception, is an electrical process. In this text I am using the word memory to refer to long-term memory, that is memories that are stored for a lifetime. Long-term memory is a chemical process involving the exchange of neuropeptides.

We know that memories are stored in the unconscious mind, but the location of the mind is inconclusive. Although thoughts can be measured as brain waves, this does not mean that the mind is part of the brain. The brain is the interface between our thoughts and the resulting actions. An understanding of a few basic concepts concerning brain organisation can help this interface to work more efficiently and enrich your life.

Your brain works best when it is slightly cooler than what we usually consider as room temperature. It is better for your memory if your environment is comfortably cool, where you probably need to wear a jumper, rather than a warm or hot environment. Good posture helps blood and oxygen to circulate to the brain. Your mental capacity is boosted by regular breaks from the task in hand, especially if they involve some kind of body movement that boosts circulation.

The brain consists of two hemispheres, the right and the left. Information flows between the hemispheres via a bundle of nerve fibres called the corpus callosum. Although there are biological differences in the way men and women process data, the information below is general enough to apply to both genders. Each hemisphere usually deals with quite different aspects of processing, as indicated in Figure 2.

Left		**Right**
Logical		Creative
Analytical		Spatial
Sequential		Patterns
Language		Music
Time		Visual
Detail		'Big picture'
Controls right side of body		Controls left side of body
Masculine aspect		Feminine aspect

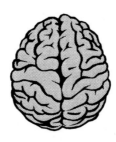

Figure 2. Functions of the two hemispheres of the brain

For almost everyone, one side of the brain is dominant, meaning we use it more often and in preference to the other side. We all have masculine and feminine aspects to us, so men are not necessarily left-brain dominant and women are not necessarily right-brain dominant.

The hemispheres control the opposite side of the body because of the way the nerves cross over at the back of the brain. If you are right-handed, you probably use the right side of your body more and therefore stimulate the left hemisphere more often. Whenever you talk, or think in words, you are stimulating the left hemisphere. Our culture encourages punctuality and time-awareness, which are also left brain functions. The technology that is part of our lives usually requires us to be logical and analytical in order to use it.

Traditional science is logical, analytical and detailed. It usually receives more respect in our society than the artistic and creative endeavours that originate from the right hemisphere. There is a tendency to demand hard facts supported by scientific study before the majority of people accept something to be true.

As soon as we enter the education system we have to adhere to a timetable of lessons. We learn to read and write language. We are taught lots of details using sequential, ordered techniques. In our early years when we are so impressionable, our left hemisphere receives plenty of stimulation while our right hemisphere seems to be neglected. It is to our detriment that we are not taught how to use the full capacity of our minds efficiently.

There have been attempts to include more physical education and music in the curriculum. PE and games encourage spatial awareness, which is a right-brain activity, but this usually makes up a very small percentage of overall lesson time in most schools. Even the study of music is often reduced to analysing notes and phrases, the sort of detail that is more likely to stimulate the left hemisphere.

So left-brain dominance is encouraged in our society. Individuals who demonstrate the so-called masculine and therefore left-hemisphere qualities of strength and control are usually respected. Despite recent advances in equal opportunities, stereotyping and discrimination against females and feminine qualities still exist. Some people may argue that many of our technological advancements were a result of logic, analysis and attention to detail, all left-brain qualities. However, it almost always requires the creativity and innovation from the right hemisphere to conceive the ideas for these advancements.

Computers are very good at most of the left hemisphere attributes. They can perform logical, analytical and sequential operations very quickly. They are not so good at the right hemisphere attributes such as visual recognition, spatial awareness, music and creativity. I believe that we can advance further by enhancing our right-brain functioning and leaving some of the number-crunching and analysis to computers.

If you predominantly use one side of your brain you are limiting yourself. If you want to make the most of your potential and enrich your life, your goal should be to aim for more whole-brain functioning. This means using the qualities of both sides in most of the things you do. For the majority of people, the way to do this is to stimulate the right hemisphere.

This book presents some topics that are abstract and that science cannot yet explain, and often challenges generally accepted logic. For this reason, I suspect it will have greater appeal to those who use their right hemisphere more than the average person. If you believe you tend to use your whole brain in most situations or are right-brain dominant, the suggestions below can still be beneficial. Note that left-handedness does not guarantee right-brain dominance.

For each experience you have in life, you have the opportunity to integrate the information into your memory. I use the term learning to refer to the integration of these experiences because there is something to learn from every situation. How much you learn depends to some extent on how much of your brain you are using. For example, you may think you have taken in all the details of a particular situation, but you may have failed to recognise the holistic aspect; the 'big picture'.

Memories are stored as networks of associations. The more paths you have to a particular memory, the more likely you are to be able to recall it on demand. We learn and remember by associating new experiences with stored memories, thus giving context to the new information. This means that the more you learn and store from each experience, the more information you have to draw on in the future.

You can improve your memory by making more connections, more pathways. The more you have learnt, the easier it is to learn new things because the network is bigger. There is no truth in the suggestion that your memory can 'fill up' or that memory declines with age. Making the most of your memory and increasing the number of connections become easier when you use your whole brain to learn as much from each experience as possible.

Probably the simplest way to stimulate both sides of your brain and encourage communication between them is via your body. In most exercises your body strives for physical balance. When you walk, your left arm swings forward as you step out with your right leg, and vice versa. Brisk walking, running, swimming and cycling are all good ways to encourage whole-brain functioning. Racquet sports or other exercises where one side of the body is used more than the other also stimulate both sides of the brain because your whole body is involved, but are not so good as more balanced exercises.

If you are struggling to solve a problem, perhaps sitting at a desk, it may be that you are not using the full potential of your brain. You may find it helpful to stand up and walk around for a few minutes to encourage whole-brain thinking. If this is not possible you can use the following exercise as a substitute. Lift your left leg slightly while using your right hand to tap your left knee. Then lift your right leg and tap your right knee with your left hand. Continue alternating in this way for at least a minute.

Just using the opposite side of the body from usual can increase whole-brain functioning. For example, you could fold your arms with the other arm on top, hold your pen in the other hand or move your mouse to the other side of the computer. When you start to walk you could step out with the other leg first or you could sit down on your chair from the other side. The left hemisphere loves routine and order, so changing habitual patterns can help stimulate the right hemisphere and create new associations.

Classical music, and particularly the forms and patterns of compositions from the baroque period, activates the right hemisphere and is a very good learning aid. Vision is a right-brain activity, so cultivating a vivid imagination and using visualisation can also be beneficial.

A technique I find very useful is mind mapping. A mind map is a pictorial representation of a topic in a way that reflects the organisation of memory. This can be used when deciding on a course of action, resolving problems, planning, or organising your thoughts.

To create a mind map, start with a blank sheet of paper and

some coloured pens or pencils. Write a word to represent the topic you are exploring in the centre of the paper. For each aspect of the topic, draw a line radiating from the centre and write a word or draw a symbol on it that represents the aspect. A cue word is all that is required – grammatically correct sentences add unnecessary detail. Use different colours and use curved lines some of the time. For things that are particularly important, make the word or picture stand out in some way, perhaps using bright colours or making it large or bold.

You can then use the same technique of radiating lines to explore each of the different aspects to add more detail, building up a diagram of associations. The idea of the mind map is that it allows spontaneous thought, so it doesn't have to be planned. As you build up the mind map, you will probably find that it stimulates relevant thoughts that contribute to the subject

So if you were deciding where to go on holiday, for example, you might have the word HOLIDAY in the centre and lines for the things you want from the holiday such as relaxation, water sports, scenery, entertainment and accommodation. Pictures appeal to the right hemisphere, so you could draw a picture of your favourite water sport rather than writing the words. You could add more lines from the water sports line for each of the activities you fancy.

It is easy to add thoughts to the mind map by just drawing and labelling more lines. If you see connections between different parts of the mind map, you can draw a line to link them. As the words and the visual appeal of the mind map prompt new ideas, you can simply add them where appropriate. This allows non-sequential thinking and activates the memory in a way that is more compatible with its natural processing than linear note-taking.

In the holiday example, when you have finished adding your requirements, you could look for a general theme. If you have written or drawn 'peaceful' and 'quiet' several times, it probably indicates that a clubbing holiday is not for you. The things that are important should stand out and may reveal the most appropriate holiday destination.

As memory is a chemical process, anything that affects the

delicate chemical balance of the body could interfere with memory. You may notice that when you are in a state of panic, you cannot remember things that you can usually recall easily. Anything that causes stress hormones to be produced such as fear, panic or anxiety can inhibit your memory. Even the sort of stress associated with work situations can cause a decline in memory functioning, so relaxation is an aid to memory. Worrying if you can meet that work deadline will probably make you work less efficiently.

The unconscious mind will distract your concentration if your basic needs are not met. If you are hungry, thirsty or uncomfortable, you will probably find it more difficult to learn and remember things because your unconscious mind keeps bringing bodily sensations into your awareness. For optimum memory functioning, it is usually more efficient to take a break to attend to these physical needs rather than trying to ignore them until you have finished.

If there is something you have to commit to memory, perhaps some facts you find uninteresting, using right hemisphere functions will help. If you can create a phrase or poem from the facts with rhythm and rhyme, these patterns will stimulate the right brain. Some people remember the colours of the rainbow using the phrase 'Richard of York gained battle in vain' (the first letter of each word indicates the colour). You may be familiar with the poem that describes the number of days in each month.

As music is processed in the right hemisphere, singing phrases or poems increases the stimulation, which is why children are often taught to sing the alphabet. Have you noticed how you are able to recall the lyrics of a song that you have not heard for years?

If you can generate visual images easily, I recommend making up a visual story incorporating what you have to learn. Your right hemisphere responds well to symbolism and metaphor, so the story does not have to be literal. Images have huge potential for detail and allow adding meaning to bland facts. If you are learning about William the Conqueror, your story could include a man having a conker fight, for example.

The more emotive and interesting you make your learning, the more successful it will be. Ensure learning is fun by adding humour where possible. You can make boring or serious facts more memorable by generating cartoon images or ridiculous scenes and adding amusing sound effects. Make your phrases or poems rude if it helps you remember them. They are for your benefit and you don't need to share them with anyone else.

The memories you have accumulated throughout your life determine your decisions and your reactions. In some cases this is good because it allows you to guide yourself towards pleasurable experiences and avoid pain. However, as discussed in previous chapters, memories are stored based on biased perceptions and can become distorted over time. Many memories were formed in infancy when your immature mind did not understand the situation. If the memories of particular incidents have a negative influence on you, you can probably benefit by changing them.

If you can remember the incident, work out which aspect of it caused the unpleasant or negative repercussions. For example, being falsely accused of misbehaving at school and made to stand in the corner or humiliated in some way in front of the class, could affect your self-esteem to this day. The issue may have been the false accusation, not being listened to, not trusted, or having your classmates stare at you. With the experience and maturity you have now, you could probably explain the truth calmly and logically, or at least recognise it was the teacher who was at fault, not you.

In order to change the memory, you have to be able to relive the incident and make it as real as possible. Instead of reacting in the way you recall, you can imagine you are reasoning with your accuser or clarifying the situation. Then you can create the events immediately following it to fit in with the new reaction. Remember, your unconscious mind does not recognise the difference between what is real and what is imagined.

To do this, go into a deeply relaxed state as described in Chapter Seventeen. Go back in time to the incident in a way that feels right for you. You may imagine floating above the time line of your life, going into the past and dropping down into the appropriate event. Or you may imagine being transported back through time in some other way.

Imagine the incident in as much detail as possible, adding images, sounds, feelings and tastes if appropriate. Ensure you are part of the scene and you are experiencing it as if you were there right now. If you have the tendency to dissociate from the events as if you are an observer, you can create the scene in detail, then step into the 'you' that you are observing, becoming part of the scenario as you do so.

Relive the incident exactly as you remember it until it comes to the part that has affected you so deeply. At this point, imagine you are reacting in a mature and appropriate way to diffuse the situation. Make this realistic to the circumstances – your voice will sound as it did at the time, you will have the physical attributes you had then; the only thing that is different is that your reaction is controlled and mature. In this way your mind is more likely to accept the scenerio as real and replace the old memory. Imagine a positive reaction and allow the incident to draw to a satisfactory conclusion.

Allow yourself to feel good about the situation. Intensify the feelings and let them spread throughout your body. Keep this feeling as you bring yourself slowly back into the present.

If you do this thoroughly and with commitment, you probably only need to do it once. Accept the process is complete and carry on with life as usual. Don't dwell on the exercise. You may not feel any different at first, but after several weeks you may be aware that you have reacted differently to certain situations since the exercise. At the time it just felt normal, because the new memory is an integrated part of you. Sometimes changing a memory in this way will make subtle changes to all your interactions.

You may still be able to remember the original memory, but it will be more vague than the new memory. You can assist the old memory to fade by making the images blurred, dull and smaller, the sounds quieter and less distinct, and the feelings detached. You may think it could cause problems if you have a different recollection of events from other people involved in the incident, but the chances are they all have different perspectives and memories of it anyway.

By modifying your memories you change your reality and create new possibilities for yourself. This can be a very powerful process. The information described above can help you improve your memory and bring more control into your life. You may find relationships improve as you are able to remember events and shared experiences more clearly. People usually appreciate it when you can recall details about them or things they have said.

Remember that your unconscious mind interprets your habitual thoughts and words as instructions. If you think you have a terrible memory, or you often apologise at meetings saying you are 'hopeless at remembering names', this is what your unconscious mind will deliver. Change this attitude now and recognise that your memory is incredibly powerful, with a practically limitless capacity. Using the techniques described in this chapter can help you make the most of it.

Chapter 21

Illness

Illness is usually regarded as the opposite of wellness. However, there are various degrees of wellness and illness. I know people who are reliant on medication, or have many aches and pains, or have frequent colds and coughs who regard themselves as healthy. I even know two people who are fitted with pacemakers who think they are healthy. Illnesses that can be controlled with medication such as diabetes or hypothyroidism are still major illnesses.

There appears to be a tendency to dismiss common illnesses as acceptable or even normal if it affects a large percentage of the population. High blood pressure, obesity and defective vision are just a few of the conditions that are often disregarded. In some ways, a positive attitude in the face of illness is a good thing as will be discussed later. But to deny there is anything wrong or to refuse to acknowledge signs of illness is irresponsible.

Most people regard illness as an annoying inconvenience that interferes with their normal life. They do everything they believe they can to recover as quickly as possible, which often includes taking drugs. However, illness is an important message from your unconscious mind and should be accepted with gratitude. If you resist this idea you risk compromising your health.

You may think that it is inevitable that you will catch a virus if the other members of your family have it, or that you are just unlucky. However, there are germs all around us all the time. We are all exposed to bacteria and viruses every day, but only some people become ill with the disease. So why do you become ill when you do? There are several possible reasons.

Your diet and lifestyle play an important part in your health. There are hereditary or genetic factors that could make you more susceptible to certain illnesses, but these are much less significant than your lifestyle. The reason that illnesses tend to run in families is that the family members often follow a similar lifestyle and have similar beliefs about health. A recent radio report said that genetic factors are relevant in fewer than 5 per cent of cases of breast cancer.

Your personality affects your susceptibility to illness. Relaxed, laid-back people are categorised as having a type A personality. People who are highly competitive, restless, set high personal goals and are often irritable are categorised as type B. Type B personalities are typically high achieving, stressed-out business people. Psychologists and the medical profession recognise that type B personalities are much more likely to suffer with high blood pressure, blocked arteries and cardiovascular diseases, among other things.

The type C personality has now also been identified. People who hold in their emotions and do not express themselves fall into the type C category. Emotions are energy, and if this energy is not released it builds up in the body over time. The energy associated with intense or persistent negative emotions can have a detrimental effect on the major organs of the body. Type C personalities are more prone to cancers. The suppressed energy of negative emotions literally eats away at the body from the inside.

Your thoughts cause actions within the body and your thoughts and attitudes are factors in your health. Patterns of thinking can cause patterns of illness. The neuropeptides that are involved in the thought process and memory have also been measured within the cells of the body, indicating that cells hold memories. This seems to be the scientific proof of what complementary therapists have known for thousands of years. Your mind and body are one.

I believe that all illness is a message from your unconscious mind. The common cold is a short illness that usually forces you to rest for a day or two. You may acknowledge that you were tired or 'run down' when you caught it. The preceding tiredness may have been a signal from your unconscious mind to rest, but this was apparently ignored, so your unconscious mind sent a stronger message; the cold. You could ignore this message too by dosing yourself up with drugs instead of resting, but don't be surprised if an even stronger and more debilitating message follows.

As we have already explored, your unconscious mind communicates with you in metaphors. Perhaps you did not feel particularly tired when you last had a cold, but it was a real 'streamer' producing excess mucus and causing your eyes to stream. This could be your unconscious mind forcing you to release some emotions as you would in crying. You may recognise that you recently held back tears and didn't express your sadness. You should be very grateful for this. If the emotions remained trapped in your body they could cause much more serious illness.

Sports injuries are an excellent example of your unconscious mind protecting you from serious harm. Perhaps you had been training hard or playing competitively and overstretched yourself, resulting in a muscle strain. The muscle strain forces you to rest while the muscle repairs itself. If you had honoured the limitations of your body you could have continued playing or training, and the message from your unconscious mind would not have been necessary.

It is important to understand that you do not suddenly become ill or injured. The conditions for illness or disease build up gradually. This could be in the form of poor diet, lifestyle or destructive thoughts. The sudden pain, attack or inflammation is the outward expression of an ongoing internal process that has reached breaking point.

As your unconscious mind is in control of your body, it is reasonable to assume that it is directing your lifestyle. Your mind influences your choice of food and drink and your exercise regime, or lack of it. So if your lifestyle is less than ideal, it is probably best to address the unconscious reasons why. It could be that you continue with this lifestyle out of habit (the unconscious mind likes routine), or it could be that your negative thoughts are affecting your actions. The best of conscious intentions can be sabotaged by the unconscious mind if it thinks it is protecting you.

A good example of this is the notion of dieting to 'lose weight'. Some people who feel they are fat want to become slim.

The first mistake they make is to believe they want to lose weight. The unconscious mind registers the word 'weight', as discussed in Chapter Twelve. They are concentrating on what they want to lose, rather than what they want to gain. They view the diet as a restriction and eat to a defined limit, or avoid certain foods.

A better way to approach the issue would be to explore why the unconscious mind encouraged overeating or taking too little exercise in the first place. There are many reasons, and a common one is a feeling of insecurity or being unlovable. The layers of fat become something to hide behind and act as buffers to prevent anyone or anything coming too close. The person feels safer wearing their protective armour of fat. Being overweight can then be regarded as a psychological issue and one that can be addressed by the mind.

And so it is with all illnesses. If you realise that all diseases and conditions are caused by your thoughts and beliefs, you have the opportunity to heal them. You can choose to accept this philosophy and take responsibility for your health, or you can reject it, thinking that good health is just a matter of luck. I believe that your body always tends towards good health and it is only the intervention of negative thoughts that causes illness. If you always hold positive thoughts and are at ease with yourself, you will not suffer from dis-ease.

The usual response to pain or illness is to visit a doctor. The doctor then attaches a name to it, sometimes unpronounceable, giving the impression it is something mysterious and outside your control. He or she will probably then prescribe some drugs to suppress the symptoms. This course of action denies the role of the mind in the illness and takes away some of your responsibility for recovery. It also masks the valuable message from your unconscious mind.

When patients believe the medical profession is in control, the outcome of their treatment is influenced by the reactions and attitudes of the surgeon, doctor and nurses. Statistically, patients given a positive prognosis respond better to treatment than those given a negative prognosis, regardless of the seriousness of their condition. Even the words of surgeons and doctors while the patient is unconscious affect the outcome.

Almost anything that happens within your body is under your control. All your internal processes are affected by your thoughts. The placebo effect is a demonstration of how your mind can heal your body. If you believe a pill or therapy will cure you, your mind will create the necessary healing, regardless of whether it is a powerful drug or just sugar and water. Similarly, if you believe your condition is incurable or that the therapy will be ineffective, that is what you will manifest. Your mind is powerful enough to create healing, even from illnesses normally considered as terminal.

Your cells are regenerating continually, so any damage should be repaired within a short time as long as you create the right conditions for healing. However, even with optimal physical conditions, healing may not follow if you do not address the emotional issues behind the illness. Or you may find you recover from one illness, only to become ill with something else shortly afterwards. This could be the same message in a different guise.

The interpretation of the meaning behind illness and disease is similar to that described in Chapter Nineteen. The way the illness manifests itself can help you understand the message. People with the same illness as diagnosed by a doctor can have different symptoms and reactions. Even if their symptoms are the same, the message the illness represents is personal and therefore can be different for each person.

As with all messages from your unconscious mind, they are personal, and you have to interpret them and work out how they relate to your life and current situation. The examples I am providing here are to give you ideas and may not be relevant to you. However, they are very common metaphors, so don't reject them just because you don't want to admit your true feelings. Learning about yourself requires honesty, and the truth can sometimes be painful at first.

If you were consciously aware of the issues, your unconscious mind would not need to create the illness or condition. The point of the communication is to inform you or remind you about something outside your awareness. It may therefore take some deep and honest searching to understand the message. Understanding the meaning may just be the start. You may have to do some inner exploration and personal awareness exercises to release the underlying cause of the illness.

Most illnesses cause a change or restriction in your lifestyle and the message could be in the changes required. If you have to slow down as a result of the illness, it may be that you need to slow down in other areas of your life. Perhaps you are pressing forward too quickly with a project or decision that could affect you adversely. Or the change in circumstances could give you a different perspective on an aspect of your life, or give you time to ponder on something important.

Consider what the affected part of the body does for you. For example, if you have a sore throat, it is probably difficult or painful for you to talk. You may find it difficult to communicate or to express yourself. This could be a message that you need to express yourself more or make yourself heard in a particular situation. Conversely, it could be that you are speaking too much or interfering in some way. You may be failing to take into account someone else's opinion, and the silence caused by your sore throat forces you to listen.

If you have a loud or hacking cough, it could be an indication that you want to shout out something. Is there something you want to say but are holding back? Does your cough become worse in certain situations or in the presence of particular people?

Swelling or inflammation could be a way of protecting you from the outside world. It could be a sign of unrecognised vulnerability, so your body produces some protective padding. Inflammation can also represent something bubbling up and ready to explode. If it is accompanied by redness it could indicate unexpressed anger, as red is often associated with anger.

The way you describe your illness also provides a clue as to the meaning of it. If you say you have a rash, it could be that you are making a rash decision. I have heard people describing their 'angry rash' when it is particularly severe. Others may say they have skin sensitivity, which could indicate they are particularly sensitive to a certain issue without fully realising. The skin is your physical contact with the outside world.

People who say they are 'pissed off' with something may suffer urinary problems. Those that claim to be 'fed up' may find they have excess fat. If you say you are 'sick and tired' of something, this may be reflected in your illness. Communication with your unconscious mind goes both ways, so if you use similar phrases frequently, they may be interpreted as instructions.

A headache is often a sign that you are thinking too much and ignoring your intuition. The logical course of action may not necessarily be the best one for you. It may be that you need to take more notice of your feelings and follow your heart rather than your head. Or it could be a sign that you are using your intellect and ignoring the physical sensations and requirements of your body.

Problems with vision could indicate there is something you do not want to see. The word 'see' in this context could be metaphoric and refer to something you can't understand or won't admit to. It may indicate there is an aspect of yourself that you are refusing to accept. You may want to retreat from a situation by making everything appear further away or distorted, or just make everything a blur so you can ignore it. If you wear corrective lenses, the issues that resulted in visual disturbances may have been resolved years ago, but the distortion is maintained by the lenses, as described in Chapter Seven.

Similarly, hearing problems can occur when there is something you don't want to hear. A friend of mine had meningitis when he was five, resulting in total hearing loss. Just before he became ill, his parents argued a great deal and would shout at each other very loudly. It is feasible that his young mind thought "I don't want to hear my parents arguing" and his unconscious mind obliged by making him deaf. He obviously didn't want to become deaf, but perhaps his unconscious mind thought it was protecting him from the pain of his parents' rows.

Your neck, shoulders and back are involved in supporting and carrying yourself. Some people talk about 'shouldering burdens', or complain that 'work is back-breaking'. People or situations are often referred to as 'a pain in the neck'. These phrases that we have adopted in our language are an indication of the way our thoughts are reflected in our body. Problems in these areas commonly occur in people who are feeling the 'weight of responsibility'.

The hips and legs are used for moving forward. Conditions that restrict your movement could indicate a fear of moving forward in life. Are your emotions preventing you from making progress? Is there a situation you want to walk away from? Feet allow you to step out or 'put your best foot forward'. Are you frightened to take the first step in something? These are all metaphors that require your own interpretation relevant to your life.

The heart is associated with love and compassion. Heart problems may reflect a lack of love, either for someone else or for yourself. Do you allow enough love into your life? Do you love yourself? The heart circulates blood around your body and circulation problems could be related to 'being out of circulation'. Do you socialise much? Do you extend your love to your family and friends?

Asthma and breathing problems may be an indication that you are feeling smothered. Are you being restricted to such an extent that you have no room to breathe? Or perhaps you are so submerged in something that you have not even given yourself time to 'come up for air'. In situations of stress and panic our breathing is often restricted. Are you living in a state of constant panic and anxiety? Take a deep breath and relax.

The stomach allows us to absorb things. If you have stomach problems, consider if there is something you 'can't stomach' or that makes you sick when you think about it. Are there things you are not willing to take in and accept? Diarrhoea is a method of rejecting unacceptable food. Do you reject some ideas immediately in the same way? Are you ignoring something important? An upset stomach could indicate you are upset about a particular situation. An ulcer may be a sign that you are allowing an unresolved issue to 'eat away at you'.

The urinary system and bowels help eliminate waste from your body. Enlarged prostate or constipation could mean you are holding on to something you should let go of. Are you clinging to toxic thoughts? Is there something that you would be better off releasing?

Hands reach out, hold, grip and cling. Hand problems may be an indication that you feel you are 'losing your grip' (losing control of a situation) or reaching out for help to no avail. Fingers provide dexterity and control and can point out details. Are you concentrating too much on details and ignoring the 'big picture'? Perhaps there is a situation in which you would be better off relinquishing control or trusting others to resolve.

Depression and mental illness, including anxiety and phobias, often reflect conflict between the conscious and unconscious minds. You are being pulled in two different directions, resulting in confusion. For example, you may be following your career or lifestyle because it is the family tradition. Perhaps it was always assumed that you would continue this tradition, so much so that you never consciously questioned it or considered whether there were alternatives. The complexities of relationships can also be a source of conflict, as discussed in Chapter Sixteen. Take time to feel the sensations of your body and listen to your intuition. What is it you really want? It may help to examine your true motivations as discussed in Chapter Fourteen and use some of the techniques described elsewhere in this book.

The above examples are designed to give you an idea of how to start interpreting the messages that have manifested themselves as illness or disease. Illness is just one aspect of your life and you will probably find it easier to make sense of its meaning by taking into account other events in your life, including your dreams. See the Further Reading section for books that cover this subject in more detail.

Once you think you understand the issue that caused your ill-health or have a clue to it, you can use any of the techniques described elsewhere in this book to address it or explore it in more detail. You may choose affirmations, visualisation, emotional release, relaxation, writing or expression, whichever is most appropriate for you. If you have no idea what the message behind your illness is, ask your unconscious mind for help using any of the above methods.

I know of some programmes that advocate imagining battles within the body in order to drive out the invader or kill the bad cells. Visualisation in this way can be very powerful and result in healing, but in battles, there are often casualties from the 'good' side. I prefer methods that resolve the issues peacefully. This is especially relevant when dealing with cell mutation such as in cancer or degenerative disease. Any 'bad' cells are part of you, so to fight them is to reject a part of yourself. Imagining internal disruption and agitation may not provide the optimum conditions for healing.

If you want to use visualisation to promote healing, I recommend imagining the affected part being supplied with everything required for healing, and the tissues forming into perfect health. You don't need to know what you look like internally to do this, because the unconscious mind communicates symbolically. You can use any image that you clearly recognise as the area to be healed. You can imagine tiny people helping with the repair, or turning dials to regulate heart rate, circulation or metabolism, or whatever representation feels appropriate to you.

Accidents can be interpreted in the same way as illness. If you drop a hammer on your toe, you may class it as an accident, but you were holding the hammer and it was your failure to hold it adequately that caused you to let go. You had total control over the situation and it was solely your actions, presumably unconscious, that resulted in the incident. Your unconscious mind created the 'accident' in order to send you a message.

It took me a while to accept this concept. I damaged my finger once when catching a basketball thrown by one of my team mates. I thought it wasn't my fault and reasoned that the ball had been thrown too high and in the wrong position. But I had created the circumstances for the incident by choosing to play in the team and being in that particular place at the time. I was totally in control of my actions to catch the ball. My unconscious mind caused the injury on that particular finger as a message.

Even situations you regard as out of your control are choreographed by your unconscious mind. The unconscious communication between us all draws you to certain places and into specific events. You may think you were just innocently walking down the street when someone ran into you, but why were you there at that exact time? Your energy interacted with the environment. You were attracted to the situation because it created an important message for you. This is synchronicity.

If you accept that there is a message in every illness, injury, 'accident' or event, you can start to take more control of your life. Some of your unconscious motives become conscious and you become more self-aware. When you begin to recognise the meaning of the minor ailments and inconveniences in your life and take action to resolve the issues, more serious illnesses become unnecessary. Learning from your condition or illness is an important part of your future health and happiness.

Conclusion

Your unconscious mind creates and controls all aspects of your life to a certain extent. Many processes and motivations will remain unconscious, yet may have significant implications for you. Old behaviour patterns and emotional baggage may be directing your life in ways you would prefer to avoid.

The more you can understand about your reality, emotions and the way you store and process information, the greater conscious control you have. If you can recognise the reasons behind your reactions and behaviours, you increase the possibility of changing them. When you can resolve the issues and beliefs that are interfering with your desires, your life flows more freely and you can bring more health and happiness into it.

As you recognise the messages your unconscious mind is sending you, you can take greater responsibility for yourself. You gain more insight and decrease the requirement for stronger signals that could manifest themselves as unpleasant situations, accidents or illness. By learning to communicate with your unconscious mind, you can deepen your understanding and create what you want for yourself. I have described many ways you can do this, and I recommend you experiment to find the ones that work best for you.

Relationships can provide many challenges because the people you meet act as mirrors, reflecting the aspects of yourself that are outside your awareness. You can learn a great deal about yourself from your close relationships, and you can help others gain insight into themselves by demonstrating love and acceptance. Communication and compromise are the key requirements for successful relationships. Be considerate and remember that your behaviours affect the people and systems you are part of. Always make the best contribution you can in every situation and this will ultimately benefit you.

The journey towards self-awareness may last a lifetime, or, as some people believe, many lifetimes. Opportunities to learn more about yourself can occur at any time, so always be open to them and be grateful when they present themselves. Whatever your situation, you can choose happiness. Perhaps the most important thing to remember is to live in the 'now' and enjoy every moment. When you look after your body and mind, health and happiness come naturally.

Further Reading

Alexander, F.M. *The Use of the Self.* London: Victor Gollancz, 1992.

Andreas, Connirae & Andreas, Tamara. *Core Transformation.* Utah: Real People Press, 1994.

Ballentine, Dr Rudolph. *Radical Healing.* London: Random House, 1999.

Bates, W.H. *Better Eyesight Without Glasses.* London: Grafton, 1979.

Batmanghelidj, F. *Your Body's Many Cries for Water: A Revolutionary Natural Way to Prevent Illness and Restore Good Health.* Norwich: Tagman, 2000.

Chopra, Deepak. *Quantum Healing: Exploring the Frontiers of Mind/Body Medicine.* New York: Bantam, 1990.

Chopra, Deepak. *Unconditional Life.* London: Bantam, 1991.

Cooper, Diana. *Light Up Your Life.* Bath: Ashgrove Press, 1993.

Dethlefsen, Thorwald & Dahlke, Rudiger MD. *The Healing Power of Illness.* Shaftesbury, Dorset: Element, 1992.

Dickson, Anne. *Trusting the Tides. Self-empowerment Through our Emotions.* London: Random House, 2000.

Dyer, Wayne. *Manifest Your Destiny.* London: Thorsons, 1998.

Dyer, Wayne. *You'll See It When You Believe It.* London: Arrow, 1993.

Edwards, Gill. *Stepping Into the Magic.* London: Piatkus, 1993.

Gawain, Shakti. *Living in the Light.* London: Eden Grove, 1998.

Goodrich, Janet. *Natural Vision Improvement.* Harmondsworth: Penguin, 1996.

Groves, Barry. *Fluoride: Drinking Ourselves to Death?* Dublin: Newleaf, 2001.

Hay, Louise L. *Heal Your Body.* London: Eden Grove, 1989.

Huxley, Aldous. *The Art of Seeing.* London: Grafton, 1989.

Jones, Anne. *Heal Yourself.* London: Piatkus, 2002.

Kaplan, Robert-Michael. *The Power Behind Your Eyes.* Rochester, Vermont: Healing Arts Press, 1995.

Liberman, Jacob. *Light: Medicine of the Future.* Rochester, Vermont: Bear & Co., 1991.

Liberman, Jacob. *Take off Your Glasses and See*. NewYork: Three Rivers Press, 1995.

McDermott, Ian & O'Connor, Joseph. *NLP and Health*. **London**: Thorsons, 1996.

McTaggart, Lynne. *What Doctors Don't Tell You*. New York: Avon Books, 1999.

Murphy, Joseph. *The Power of your Unconscious Mind*. London: Simon & Schuster, 1992.

O'Connor, Joseph & Seymour, John. *Introducing NLP*. London: Thorsons, 1995.

Pease, Allan and Barbara. *Why Men Don't Listen and Women Can't Read Maps*. London: Orion, 2001

Proto, Louis. *Self Healing*. London: Piatkus, 1993.

Quackenbush, Thomas R. *Relearning to See*. Berkeley, CA: North Atlantic Books, 1997.

Roet, Dr Brian. *All in the Mind? Think Yourself Better*. London: Optima, 1994.

Rose, Colin. *Accelerated Learning*. Aylesbury: Accelerated Learning Systems Ltd, 1991.

Schneider, M. *Self Healing: My Life and Vision*. London: Arkana, 1989.

Silva, Jose & Stone, Robert B. *You the Healer*. Tiburon, CA: H J Kramer, 1989.

Silverthorn, Julie and Overdurf, John. *Dreaming Realities*. Carmarthen: Crown House Publishing, 2000.

Tolle, Eckhart. *The Power of Now*. London: Hodder & Stoughton, 2001.

Watson, Lyall. *Supernature II*. London: Hodder & Stoughton, 1986.

Wilde, Stuart. *Infinite Self*. Carlsbad, CA: Hay House, 1996.

Wilson, Timothy. *Strangers to Ourselves*. Harvard: Belknap, 2002.